Successful
health and safety
management

HSG65

HSE BOOKS

Contents

Contents

Contents

Foreword

Successful health and safety management (HSG65) was first prepared by HSE's Accident Prevention Advisory Unit (now Operations Unit) in 1991 as a practical guide for directors, managers, health and safety professionals and employee representatives who wanted to improve health and safety in their organisations.

The message it conveys is a simple one: organisations need to manage health and safety with the same degree of expertise and to the same standards as other core business activities, if they are effectively to control risks and prevent harm to people.

The publication has been a best-seller for HSE, and has been well received as providing sound guidance on good practice in health and safety management. Some of the actions it advocates go beyond what is strictly required by legislation. For example, although some specific health and safety legislation requires auditing, there is no general legal requirement to audit. Similarly there is no legal requirement to give 'tool-box talks'.

A continuing priority for HSE is to secure more effective management of health and safety by duty holders. Safety representatives and employees as well as managers can make key contributions. Together with legal requirements, the framework described here provides the basis for the approach which HSE inspectors take when auditing an organisation's arrangements for managing health and safety.

I commend this guidance to you as a tried and tested basis on which to build your health and safety management system.

Justin McCracken, Deputy Chief Executive (Operations), Health and Safety Executive

Introduction

The Health and Safety Commission's initiative to review HSE guidance has provided the opportunity to revise and update this publication. The revision does not alter the basic framework for managing health and safety set out in earlier editions, which received widespread acceptance.

The guidance is aimed at directors, managers with health and safety responsibilities, as well as health and safety professionals. Employees' representatives should also find it helpful. It:

■ describes the principles and management practices which provide the basis of effective health and safety management;
■ sets out the issues which need to be addressed; and
■ can be used for developing improvement programmes, self-audit or self-assessment.

The principles are universal but how far action is needed will depend on the size of the organisation, the hazards presented by its activities, products or services, and the adequacy of its existing arrangements.

The format follows that of previous editions. Chapter 1 provides an overview, while other chapters cover each key element in detail. Chapter 4, on planning and implementing, has been extensively revised and new material presented. Chapter 5, on measuring performance, incorporates new material on accident and incident investigation. Chapter 6 has been amplified to add more guidance on auditing. Within each chapter, insets deal with a particular topic in more detail to avoid interrupting the flow of the main text. A short set of references is given at the end.

CHAPTER ONE

Summary

The key elements of successful health and safety management are set out in this summary. Diagram 1 outlines the relationship between them.

Policy

Effective health and safety policies set a clear direction for the organisation to follow. They contribute to all aspects of business performance as part of a demonstrable commitment to continuous improvement. Responsibilities to people and the environment are met in ways which fulfil the spirit and letter of the law. Stakeholders' expectations in the activity (whether they are shareholders, employees, or their representatives, customers or society at large) are satisfied. There are cost-effective approaches to preserving and developing physical and human resources, which reduce financial losses and liabilities.

Organising

An effective management structure and arrangements are in place for delivering the policy. All staff are motivated and empowered to work safely and to protect their long-term health, not simply to avoid accidents. The arrangements are:

- underpinned by effective staff involvement and participation; and
- sustained by effective communication and the promotion of competence which allows all employees and their representatives to make a responsible and informed contribution to the health and safety effort.

There is a shared common understanding of the organisation's vision, values and beliefs. A positive health and safety culture is fostered by the visible and active leadership of senior managers.

Planning

There is a planned and systematic approach to implementing the health and safety policy through an effective health and safety management system. The aim is to minimise risks. Risk assessment methods are used to decide on priorities and to set objectives for eliminating hazards and reducing risks. Wherever possible, risks are eliminated through selection and design of facilities, equipment and processes. If risks cannot be eliminated, they are minimised by the use of physical controls or, as a last resort, through systems of work and personal protective equipment. Performance standards are established and used for measuring achievement. Specific actions to promote a positive health and safety culture are identified.

Measuring performance

Performance is measured against agreed standards to reveal when and where improvement is needed. Active self-monitoring reveals how effectively the health and safety management system is functioning. This looks at both hardware (premises, plant and substances) and software (people, procedures and systems) including individual behaviour and performance. If controls fail, reactive monitoring discovers why by investigating accidents, ill health or incidents which could cause harm or loss. The objectives of active and reactive monitoring are:

- to determine the immediate causes of sub-standard performance; and
- to identify the underlying causes and the implications for the design and operation of the health and safety management system.

Longer-term objectives are also monitored.

Auditing and reviewing performance

The organisation learns from *all* relevant experience and applies the lessons. There is a systematic review of performance based on data from monitoring and from independent audits of the whole health and safety management system. These form the basis of self-regulation and of complying with sections 2 to 6 of the Health and Safety at Work etc Act 1974 (HSW Act) and other relevant statutory provisions. There is a strong commitment to continuous improvement involving the constant development of policies, systems and techniques of risk control. Performance is assessed by:

- internal reference to key performance indicators; and
- external comparison with the performance of business competitors and best practice, irrespective of employment sector.

Performance is also often recorded in annual reports.

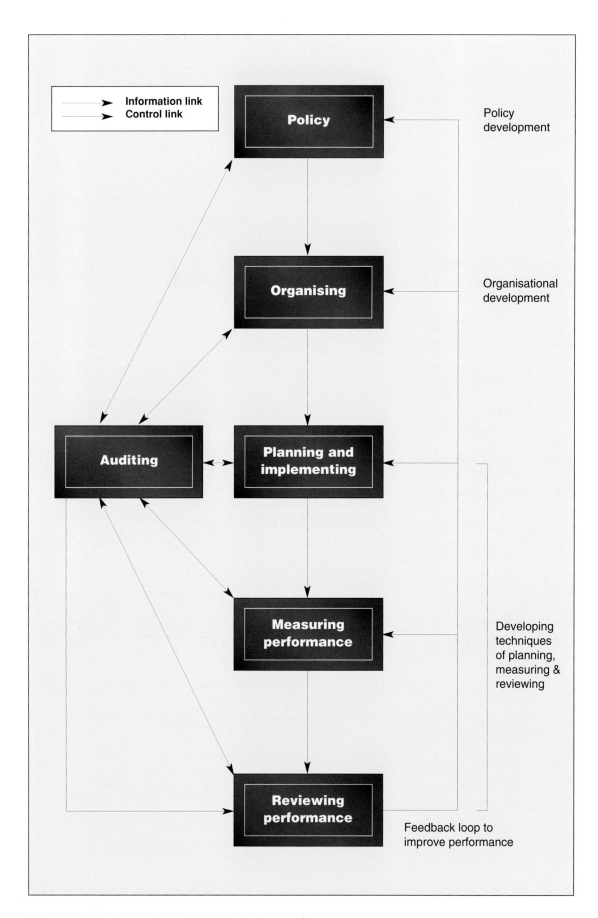

Diagram 1 *Key elements of successful health and safety management*

CHAPTER TWO

Effective health and safety policies

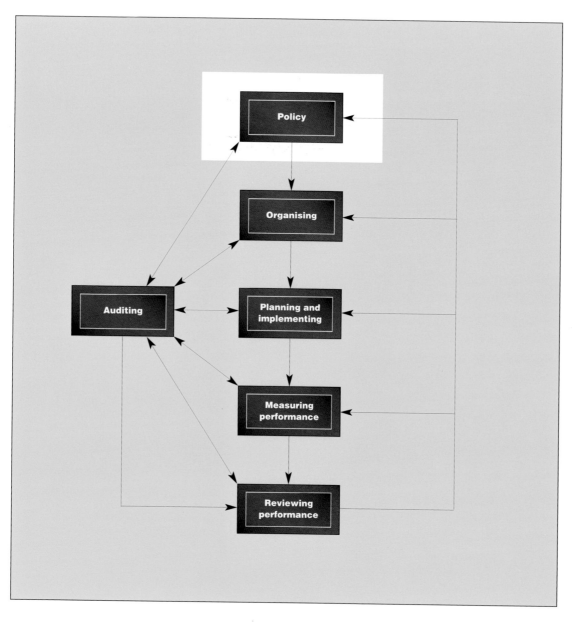

KEY MESSAGES

Effective health and safety policies contribute to business performance by:

supporting human resource development;

minimising the financial losses which arise from avoidable unplanned events;

recognising that accidents, ill health and incidents result from failings in management control and are not necessarily the fault of individual employees;

recognising that the development of a culture supportive of health and safety is necessary to achieve adequate control over risks;

ensuring a systematic approach to the identification of risks and the allocation of resources to control them;

supporting quality initiatives aimed at continuous improvement.

This chapter identifies the main characteristics of successful policies for health and safety. A common characteristic is that they accurately reflect the values and beliefs of those who devise and implement them. Effective policies are not simply examples of management paying lip service to improved health and safety performance but a genuine commitment to action. In this guidance, 'policy' means the general intentions, approach and objectives - the vision - of an organisation and the criteria and principles upon which it bases its action. These form the basis for managing health and safety which shape the written statement of policy required by section 2 of the HSW Act.

The importance of people to an organisation

Work can make a positive or negative contribution to individual health. Both physical and mental health may be affected if people are exposed to harm (eg through the use of chemicals, by a risk of falling, by carrying out repetitive tasks or being exposed to violent behaviour). But if the workplace is safe and if people are interested and involved in their work, job satisfaction can increase and improvements in health and well-being can result.

Organisations that successfully manage health and safety recognise the relationship between the control of risks, general health and the very core of the business itself. Their health and safety policies align with other human resource management policies designed to secure commitment and involvement and to promote the well-being of employees. In the workplace, this may lead to initiatives such as job restructuring - to reduce monotony and increase flexibility - or to health promotion campaigns. In some cases, organisations educate their employees about dangers outside the workplace (eg in the home) as part of an off-the-job accident prevention policy. The important contribution which employees and their representatives can make to improve health and safety is recognised and encouraged.

So the best health and safety policies do not separate health and safety and human resource management, because they acknowledge that people are the key resource. Organisations that want to behave ethically and responsibly:

- recognise the benefits of a fit, enthusiastic, competent and committed workforce;
- realise that progressive human resource management policies can be undermined by weak health and safety policies; and
- show that they are concerned not simply with preventing accidents and ill health (as required by health and safety legislation) but also with positive health promotion.

The ultimate goal is an organisation aiming to improve its health and safety performance, so that accidents and ill health are eliminated and work forms part of a satisfying life to the benefit of both the individual and the organisation. This integrated approach extends to people outside the organisation in policies for the control of off-site risks, environmental pollution and product safety.

Avoiding loss - the total loss approach

Injuries and ill health cost money but are only one component of financial loss. Accidental damage to property, plant, products or the environment - as well as production losses or liabilities - also impose costs. The total loss approach is based on research into the causes of accidents which is summarised in Inset 1. This illustrates an important relationship. There are many more incidents or 'near-misses' than those which cause injury or property damage. Effective prevention and loss control has to focus on the causes of incidents because outcomes may be random and uncontrollable. For instance, if a person slips on a patch of spilt oil they may be unhurt, damage clothing or equipment, break an arm or fracture their skull and die. Examining the causes of all such outcomes can provide valuable insights into inadequacies in risk control and point toward action which can prevent future injuries or losses (see Chapter 5).

Inset 1 **Accident ratio studies**

Several studies have tried to establish the relationship between serious and minor accidents and other dangerous events. The results of a study by HSE's Accident Prevention Advisory Unit (APAU)[1] are summarised here. The study confirmed the general validity of earlier work by Bird (1969) and Tye and Pearson (1974/75). The most significant conclusions which can be drawn from this and other research[2] are that:

- the detailed findings were different because of the definitions and accidents data used, but there is a consistent relationship between the different kinds of event;
- there are consistently greater numbers of less serious events compared to more serious ones;
- it is often a matter of chance whether dangerous events cause ill health, injury or damage. However, 'no-injury' incidents or 'near-misses' could become events with more serious consequences. Not all near-misses, however, involve risks which might have caused fatal or serious injury;
- **all** the events (not just those causing injuries) represent failures in control and are therefore potential learning opportunities.

A key feature of an effective health and safety policy is to examine all unsafe events and the behaviours which give rise to them. This is a way of controlling risk and measuring performance.

From studies in five organisations in the oil, food, construction, health and transport sectors, APAU established the following ratio:

1 major or over-3-day lost-time injury ———————————— **1**

for every 7 minor injuries ——————————— **7**

for every 189 non-injury accidents ——————— **189**

HSE is currently (1997) conducting research to link the costs of accidents with the model for health and safety management outlined in this guidance. The research aims to measure the cost of different management failures, so that organisations may better target their effort and money. The research is based on a 'root-cause analysis tool' which matches incident causes with elements of the health and safety management structure in this guidance. The tool, and findings from the research, are scheduled for publication.

The total loss approach emphasises that organisations need to learn from both accidents **and** incidents to achieve effective control. They should also look beyond their own organisation to draw lessons from elsewhere. Investment in loss reduction contributes directly to profits and may prove to be particularly cost effective at times of high competition - it may yield a better return than a similar investment to improve sales and market share. Results from HSE studies[1] of the costs of accidental loss confirm their commercial significance.

Reducing the financial costs of accidents and ill health is important in business terms, but there are other business imperatives for managing health and safety effectively. Employees benefit from working in an organisation committed to high standards of health and safety, but organisations should also recognise that there are other 'stakeholders' with a legitimate interest in how they manage health and safety. These can include shareholders, customers, suppliers, insurance companies, the neighbouring community, the public and regulators. Organisations that are successful at managing health and safety recognise the business case for health and safety and meet the different, and sometimes competing demands and expectations of their stakeholders in a balanced way.

Prime responsibility for accident and ill health prevention rests with management

Accidents, ill health and incidents are seldom random events. They generally arise from failures of control and involve multiple contributory elements. The immediate cause may be a human or technical failure, but they usually arise from organisational failings which are the responsibility of management. Successful policies aim to exploit the strengths of employees. They aim to minimise the contribution of human limitations and fallibilities by examining how the organisation is structured and how jobs and systems are designed.

Organisations need to understand how human factors affect health and safety performance. These are explained in more detail in the HSE publication HSG48 *Reducing error and influencing behaviour*[3] which also contains guidance on how to develop suitable control strategies in a systematic way (see Inset 2).

The importance of organisational factors

Organisations that are good at managing health and safety create an effective framework to maximise the contribution of individuals and groups. Health and safety objectives are regarded in the same way as other business objectives. They become part of the culture and this is recognised explicitly by making health and safety a line management responsibility. The approach has to start at the top. Visible and active support, strong leadership and commitment of senior managers and directors are fundamental to the success of health and safety management. Senior managers communicate the beliefs which underlie the policy through their individual behaviour and management practice. Health and safety is a boardroom issue and a board member takes direct responsibility for the co-ordination of effort. The whole organisation shares the management perception and beliefs about the importance of health and safety and the need to achieve the policy objectives. Examples of statements of health and safety philosophy are shown in Inset 3.

Inset 2 **Human factors in industrial health and safety**

Diagram 2 shows the relationship between the three factors that influence behaviour in organisations.

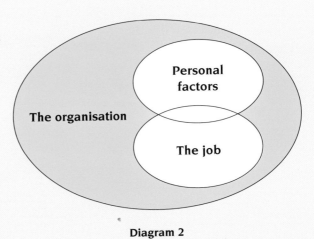

Diagram 2

Organisational factors have the major influence on individual and group behaviour, yet it is common for them to be overlooked during the design of work and when investigating accidents and incidents. Organisations need to establish their own positive health and safety culture which promotes employee involvement and commitment at all levels. This culture should emphasise that deviation from established health and safety standards is unacceptable.

Job factors directly influence individual performance and the control of risks. Tasks should be designed according to ergonomic principles to take account of the limitations of human performance. Mismatches between job requirements and individuals' capabilities increase the potential for human error. Matching the job to the individual ensures that people are not overloaded; this contributes to consistent performance. Physical matching includes how the whole workplace and the working environment are designed. Mental matching involves taking into account the individual's information and decision-making requirements as well as his or her perception of the task. Mismatches between job requirements and an individual's capabilities increase the potential for human error.

Personal factors - the attributes which employees bring to their jobs - may be strengths or weaknesses in relation to the demands of a particular task. They include both physical attributes, such as strength and limitations arising from disability or illness, and mental attributes, such as habits, attitudes, skills and personality, which influence behaviour in complex ways. Negative effects on task performance cannot always be mitigated by job design solutions. Some characteristics, such as skills and attitudes, can be modified by training and experience; others, such as personality, are relatively permanent and cannot be modified within the work context. People may therefore need to be matched to their jobs through appropriate selection techniques.

For more information, see HSG48 *Reducing error and influencing behaviour.*[3]

Inset 3 **Examples of health and safety philosophy**

'A good safety record goes hand in hand with high productivity and quality standards'

'We believe that an excellent company is by definition a safe company. Since we are committed to excellence, it follows that minimising risk to people, plant and products is inseparable from all other company objectives'

'Prevention is not only better, but cheaper than cure. There is no necessary conflict between humanitarianism and commercial considerations. Profits and safety are not in competition. On the contrary, safety is good business'

'Health and safety is a management responsibility of equal importance to production and quality'

'Experience shows that a successful safety organisation also produces the right quality goods at minimum costs'

'Competence in managing health and safety is an essential part of professional management'

'In the field of health and safety [we] seek to achieve the highest standards. We do not pursue this aim simply to achieve compliance with current legislation, but because it is in our best interests. The effective management of health and safety, leading to fewer accidents involving injury and time taken off work, is an investment which helps us to achieve our purposes'

'People are our most important asset'

'Total safety is the ongoing integration of safety into all activities with the objective of attaining industry leadership in safety performance. We believe nothing is more important than safety . . . not production, not sales, not profits'

'Effective control of health and safety is achieved through co-operative effort at all levels in the organisation'

'The company believes that excellence in the management of health and safety is an essential element within its overall business plan'

'All accidents and ill health are preventable'

'The identification, assessment and control of health and safety and other risks is a managerial responsibility and of equal importance to production and quality'

'The preservation of human and physical resources is an important means of minimising costs'

A systematic approach

The key to effective policy implementation is good business planning. The logic and rigour of business planning are applied to the control of risks, and resources are allocated according to risk priorities. The organisation is able to measure performance against plans by setting up suitable monitoring arrangements. An outline of how effective health and safety policies can affect different areas of business thinking is given in Inset 4.

Inset 4 **The impact of effective health and safety policies on business thinking**

The following areas of business thinking are among those influenced by effective health and safety policies:

Corporate strategy and social responsibility

- business mission, philosophy and codes of ethics;
- company image in the community;
- policy on environmental impact;
- management professionalism (for example, the application of the Management Charter Initiative (MCI) competences).

Finance

- loss-control and cost-reduction strategies;
- aspects of non-speculative risk management, such as product liability, security, property damage, and the consequent potential for financial loss and legal liability;
- decisions on loss reduction, risk retention or transfer, risk funding and insurance;
- investment decisions concerning business acquisitions and new premises, plant and processes;
- general financial planning and budgetary control.

Human resources

- recruitment, selection, placement, transfer, training, development and learning;
- structuring the organisation to promote a positive health and safety culture;
- work and job structuring to achieve participation and involvement;
- health promotion activities;
- communications;
- Investors in People.

Marketing, product design and product liability

- specification of product and service health and safety standards;
- national legal requirements, for example, section 6 of the HSW Act;
- international requirements such as EC directives;
- national and international consensus standards, for example, British Standards, ANSI and ISO Standards;
- the Consumer Protection Act in the case of products for domestic use.

Manufacturing and operating policy

- design, selection, construction and maintenance of premises, plant, equipment and substances;
- procurement policies including selection of contractors;
- design of jobs and the application of ergonomic principles and appropriate strategies for risk elimination, reduction and control;
- quality management;
- environmental management and waste disposal.

Information management and systems

- the identification of data critical to the management of health and safety;
- the selection of appropriate performance indicators;
- the use of information technology in the collection and analysis of essential data.

Successful organisations can demonstrate effective control in terms of improved performance. Health and safety thinking is reflected in business activity. The practical implications of health and safety policies are thought through to avoid conflict between the demands of policy and other operational requirements. Disasters - such as the sinking of the Herald of Free Enterprise, the train crash at Clapham Junction and the fire and explosion on Piper Alpha - provide vivid examples of the effect of giving insufficient attention or weight to health and safety. In these cases, management decisions led to:

- unrealistic timescales for implementing plans, which put pressure on people to cut corners and reduce supervision;
- work scheduling and rosters which failed to take account of the problems of fatigue;
- inadequate resources allocated to training;
- organisational restructuring which placed people in positions for which they had insufficient experience;
- jobs and control systems which failed to recognise or allow for the fact that people would be likely to make mistakes and might have difficulties communicating with each other.

The systematic approach also emphasises a commitment to continuous improvement. Learning from experience is essential. In many serious accidents, previous incidents foreshadowed the potential for serious injury.

Quality, environment and health and safety management

The principles and approach to managing health and safety described in this and the following chapters are the same as those advocated for managing quality or the environment. A well-developed approach to quality is increasingly seen as an essential activity for the successful organisation rather than an optional extra. Organisations often fail to manage health and safety effectively because they see it as something distinct from other management tasks. They conclude that it is too difficult. They do not bring the same rigour to it as they do for quality or the environment.

The traditional approach to ensuring quality emphasised quality control at the end of the manufacturing process: products were inspected and sorted for defects before they reached the customer. This was costly and inefficient. The modern approach is process-based quality assurance - managing quality **in** not inspecting defects **out**.

A similar case can be made for health and safety. Many organisations traditionally only react to accidents and ill health ('defects') once they have occurred. There is little emphasis on prevention. If the desired 'output' of the health and safety effort is to be achieved - to control risks - then the process to deliver it has to be properly assured through designing and implementing an effective health and safety management system. In other words it is proactive not reactive.

This approach is applied in this guidance. It is also the basis for the ISO 14001 Environmental Management standards,[4] BS 8800 *Guide to occupational health and safety management systems*[5] and the voluntary eco-management auditing schemes.[6] A word of caution is necessary though. Adopting ISO 9000 Quality Systems standards[7] will not automatically lead to appropriate attention to health and safety in the workplace. The standards focus on quality of the goods or services that the organisation produces or delivers - not on health and safety in the production or delivery process.

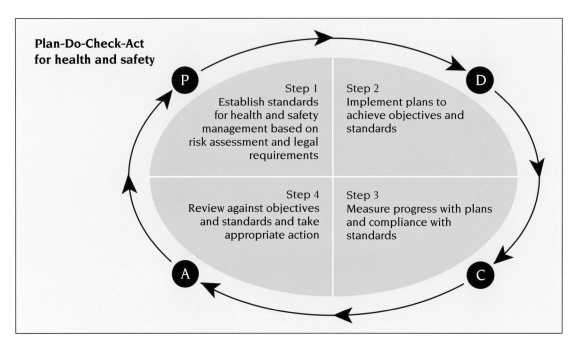

Plan-Do-Check-Act for health and safety

P

Step 1
Establish standards for health and safety management based on risk assessment and legal requirements

Step 2
Implement plans to achieve objectives and standards

D

Step 4
Review against objectives and standards and take appropriate action

Step 3
Measure progress with plans and compliance with standards

A

C

Diagram 3 *Plan-Do-Check-Act for health and safety*

Total quality management (TQM) promotes continuous improvement in all aspects of an organisation's activities. It emphasises identifying the key processes, setting performance standards, measuring achievement against these standards and then taking corrective action and identifying opportunities for improvement - all in a continuous cycle. This is often depicted as 'Plan-Do-Check-Act' and can equally be applied to health and safety (see Diagram 3).

Other areas where there is crossover between TQM methods and health and safety include:

■ the tools and techniques of TQM (eg process flowcharts, Pareto analysis, cause-and-effect diagrams) which can be applied to health and safety;

■ the development of a supportive organisational culture. The TQM philosophy stresses the importance of actively involving all employees in the quality process. It also recognises the crucial importance of visible leadership and the need for consistent emphasis on quality improvement throughout the organisation.

The business excellence model produced by the European Foundation for Quality Management (EFQM)[8] is one benchmark which organisations can use to assess their progress towards business excellence. Health and safety is recognised in this model but many organisations have yet to realise that they can use it to inform and improve their approach to the management of health and safety. HSE funded a research study[9] which examined health and safety activities in several organisations that were at various stages in implementation of TQM. One of the key findings was that visible leadership and emphasis on continual improvement with respect to health and safety lagged behind that for quality of a product or service. One reason for this finding was that senior people lacked appreciation of the business case for health and safety.

Successful organisations can establish and maintain a culture which supports health and safety. Practical ways in which they can design, build, operate and maintain the appropriate systems are examined in the following chapters.

CHAPTER THREE

Organising for health and safety

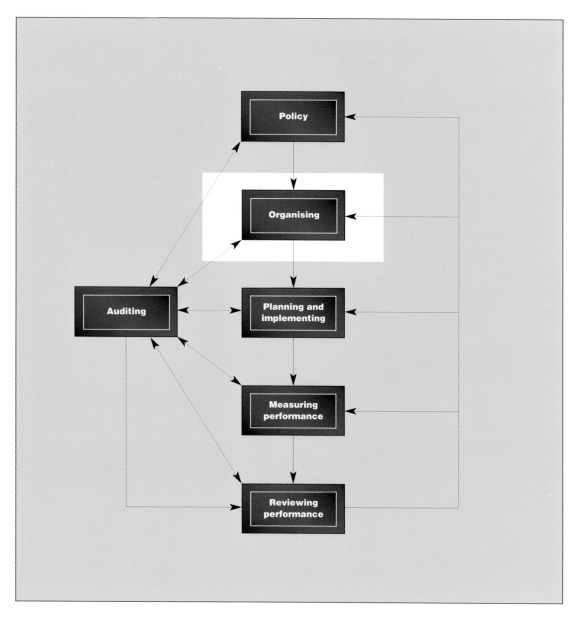

KEY MESSAGES

Organisations need to define the responsibilities and relationships which promote a positive health and safety culture, and secure the implementation and continued development of the health and safety policy. Structures and processes are needed which:

establish and maintain management control within an organisation;

promote co-operation between individuals, safety representatives and groups so that health and safety becomes a collaborative effort;

ensure the communication of necessary information throughout the organisation; and

secure the competence of employees.

The policy sets the direction for health and safety, but organisations need to create a robust framework for management activity and to detail the responsibilities and relationships which will deliver improved performance. A core element to consider is the culture of the organisation itself. There is a limit to the level of performance which can be achieved by addressing the technological and system elements of health and safety in isolation. The shared 'common knowledge' or culture unique to each organisation shapes the way it deals with health and safety issues. This culture may take years to mature but it bears on all aspects of work, affecting individual and group behaviour, job design and the planning and execution of work activities. Evidence indicates that successful companies have developed positive cultures which promote safe and healthy working.[10,11]

One definition of health and safety culture is:

'The safety culture of an organisation is the product of individual and group values, attitudes, perceptions, competencies and patterns of behaviour that determine the commitment to, and the style and proficiency of, an organisation's health and safety management.

Organisations with a positive safety culture are characterised by communications founded on mutual trust, by shared perceptions of the importance of safety and by confidence in the efficacy of preventive measures.'
(ACSNI 3rd report)[11]

Another definition is 'the way we do things around here'. By explicitly recognising the advantages in looking at their activities in this way, organisations can often achieve a step change in their approach to the management of health and safety.

In this chapter, the activities necessary to promote a positive health and safety culture are split into:

■ methods of **control** within the organisation;
■ means of securing **co-operation** between individuals, safety representatives and groups;
■ methods of **communication** throughout the organisation;
■ **competence** of individuals.

Control is the foundation of a positive health and safety culture. The management techniques for exercising control are considered in more detail in Chapters 4 to 6. The four components are, however, interrelated and interdependent so that **consistent** activity in each area is needed to promote a climate in which a positive health and safety culture can develop. Taken together, they provide the organisational framework needed to manage health and safety effectively.

Control

Establishing and maintaining control is central to **all** management functions. Control is achieved by getting the commitment of employees to clear health and safety objectives. It begins with managers taking full responsibility for controlling factors that could lead to ill health, injury or loss. The arrangements start with nominating a senior figure at the top of the organisation to co-ordinate and monitor policy implementation. Health and safety responsibilities are allocated to line managers, with specialists appointed to act as advisers. If managers provide clear direction and take responsibility for the working environment, it helps create a positive atmosphere and encourages a creative and learning culture. Safety representatives can also make an important contribution. The emphasis is on a collective effort to develop and maintain systems of control **before** the event - not on blaming individuals for failures afterwards.

Key functions for successful health and safety management can be classified into three broad areas:

■ Formulating and developing policy. This includes identifying key objectives and reviewing of progress against them.
■ Planning, measuring, reviewing and auditing health and safety activities to meet legal requirements and minimise risks.
■ Ensuring effective implementation of plans and reporting on performance.

Further details about these functions are given in Appendix 2.

These functions may not necessarily be exclusive to specific individuals or groups, so the boundaries of discretion should be established. Clear responsibilities and co-ordination are particularly important when two or more organisations work together, for example, when contractors are employed to provide goods or services within an existing establishment. If organisations are forced, or choose, to alter their internal structure in a fundamental way, there are potential effects on health and safety. HSE has carried out research[12] in this area and the results are summarised in Appendix 3.

Control arrangements are very important and should form part of the organisation's written statement on health and safety. A key part of the process of establishing control is to set performance standards which link responsibilities to outputs, recognising that the achievement of goals is based on specific, defined work with measurable outputs. It may be necessary to draw up written systems, rules or procedures to clarify the way jobs or tasks should be done to achieve the desired results. Guidelines on drawing up performance standards are given in Inset 5 with more detail in Chapter 4.

Inset 5 **Performance standards**

Performance standards are the basis of planning and measuring health and safety achievement. The maxim 'what gets measured gets done' applies. If organisations are to be efficient and effective in controlling risks, they need to co-ordinate their activities to ensure everyone is clear about what they are expected to achieve. They need to understand and specify what has to be done, both to control the direction of the organisation as a whole and to deal with specific risks.

Setting performance standards is essential if policies are to be translated from good intentions into a series of co-ordinated activities and tasks. Standards should:

- set out clearly what people need to do to contribute to an environment which is free of injuries, ill health and loss;
- help identify the competences which individuals need to fulfil their responsibilities;
- form the basis for measuring individual, group and organisational performance.

Good performance standards link responsibilities to specific outputs. They should specify:

Who is responsible?

This will give a name or position. Nobody should be made responsible for a task unless they meet suitable competence criteria (ie, they have been trained and possess the necessary skills and knowledge).

What are they responsible for?

This should explain what is to be done and how. It may involve applying specific procedures or systems of work and the use of specific documents or equipment because of legal duties. Some examples might be:

- preparing plans to implement the health and safety policy;
- carrying out risk assessments in accordance with specific regulations;
- periodic monitoring of health and safety performance;
- checking contractors' health and safety performance before awarding contracts;
- supervisor's weekly tool-box talks which may include, for example, a reminder of important health and safety procedures or lessons from a recent accident;
- providing training;
- providing first aid after an accident.

Inset 5 (*continued*)

When should the work be done?

Some work occurs regularly (eg monthly inspections) or only when particular tasks or jobs are being done (for example when using a particular chemical). A time frame should be set.

What is the expected result?

Some outputs may refer to legal requirements (eg achievement of a certain air quality standard). Alternatively, the output may be a satisfactory completion of a specified procedure (eg training). Output standards can be used to specify how individuals will be held accountable for their health and safety responsibilities.

People with specific responsibilities for health and safety should be held accountable. This may involve the use of existing personnel systems such as:

- individual job descriptions containing references to health and safety responsibilities;
- performance review and appraisal systems measuring and rewarding individual performance in health and safety activities;
- procedures identifying and acting upon failures by any employee (including managers) to achieve adequate health and safety performance. These can be integrated with normal disciplinary arrangements and be invoked when justified by the seriousness of the failure to comply.

These control arrangements are only effective if health and safety objectives get the same importance as other business aims, and if good performance by supervisors and managers is seen as vital in career progression and personal development assessments. A combination of rewards and sanctions is required to motivate all employees. There needs to be emphasis on the reinforcement of the positive behaviour which contributes to risk control and the promotion of a positive health and safety culture. The general payment and reward systems should support the achievement of health and safety objectives and avoid conflict with output and other commercial objectives. If safety award schemes are used, they need to emphasise the attainment of specific standards of performance rather than arbitrary targets or ones based solely on avoiding accidents or ill health. The better schemes reward group rather than individual effort and support a collaborative approach to health and safety management. Effective supervision is of critical importance and further guidance is contained in Inset 6.

Inset 6 **Supervision**

In organisations which emphasise effective teamworking, the term 'supervisor' may not be used because it has command and control overtones. Here the term is used to include 'team leader', or any other equivalent company designation.

Adequate supervision complements the provision of information, instruction and training to ensure that the health and safety policy of an organisation is effectively implemented and developed. Good supervision regimes can form a powerful part of a proper system of management control. There are two key aspects:

Task management

Supervisors, by example and discipline, are uniquely placed to influence how well organisations achieve health and safety objectives and what standards of performance are maintained. They can plan, direct, help, train, coach and guide staff to develop individual competence. They can also monitor performance by formal (eg assessment) and informal (spot checks) means.

Team building

Supervisors can encourage individuals to work together in pursuit of team objectives. This role can include leading team activities such as tool-box talks, team briefings and problem-solving exercises. It can also involve coaching and counselling to encourage and support the participation and involvement of employees and safety representatives. A particularly important objective is to improve understanding of the risks involved in the work and how they can be eliminated or better controlled.

It is management's job to decide on the appropriate level of supervision for particular tasks. The level depends on the risks involved as well as the competence of employees to identify and handle them. In some cases, legal requirements state minimum supervision levels. In others, more supervision may be needed, for example employees new to a job, employees undergoing training or doing jobs which present special risks, eg working alone or at shift changeovers. But some supervision of fully competent individuals will always be needed to ensure that standards are being met consistently.

Supervisors and employees should exercise judgement and discretion, for example when making decisions on when to seek help or guidance or when to halt work because they consider it too dangerous to continue. But they should exercise this discretion within the framework of control established at the top of the organisation. Although authority to act can be delegated to supervisors and employees, the ultimate responsibility for complying with the employer's legal duties cannot be delegated. It follows that management must ensure that those exercising discretion and judgement are competent to do so and have clear guidelines.

Inset 6 (*continued*)

New methods of team working - often linked to widening job content and to more flexible working arrangements - can mean, for instance, that:

■ some maintenance tasks become the responsibilities of the work group and the maintenance workers will join the production team;

■ there is increased job variety for individuals and they have to become competent in new tasks;

■ supervisors become responsible for areas of work which are outside their established expertise or experience.

Team and flexible working arrangements can increase the discretion available to supervisors and others. But where supervisors acquire wider responsibilities, they need to become familiar with new risks and with how these relate to activities of the whole group and to other groups.

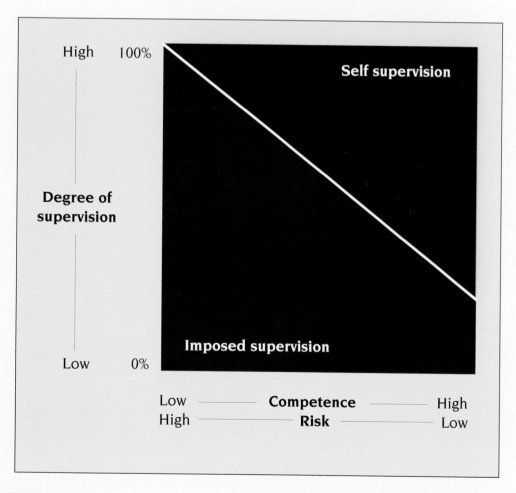

Diagram 4 *Levels of supervision*

Levels of supervision are determined by the risk of the job and the competence of the person.

Co-operation

Participation by employees supports risk control by encouraging their 'ownership' of health and safety policies. It establishes an understanding that the organisation as a whole, and people working in it, benefit from good health and safety performance. Pooling knowledge and experience through participation, commitment and involvement means that health and safety really becomes 'everybody's business'.

It is a legal requirement for all employees in Great Britain to be consulted, not just informed, about those health and safety issues in the workplace that affect them. Where trade unions are recognised, consultation must occur via the safety representatives they appoint under the Safety Representatives and Safety Committees Regulations 1977[13] and the Offshore Installations (Safety Representatives and Safety Committees) Regulations 1989.[14] All other employees not represented in this way must be consulted, either directly or via representatives elected by those employees that they represent, under the Health and Safety (Consultation with Employees) Regulations 1996.[15] All representatives must be provided with paid time off to carry out their duties and to undertake appropriate training; they must also be given adequate facilities on site.

However, successful organisations often go further than strictly required by law and **actively encourage and support consultation** in different ways. Safety representatives are trained which, in common with all employees, enables them to make an informed contribution on health and safety issues. They also enjoy the positive benefits of an open communications policy and are closely involved in directing the health and safety effort through the issues discussed at health and safety committees. Effective consultative bodies are involved in planning, measuring and reviewing performance as well as in their more traditional reactive role of considering the results of accident, ill health and incident investigations and other concerns of the moment.

Employees at all levels are also involved individually or in groups in a range of activities. They may, for example, help set performance standards, devise operating systems, procedures and instructions for risk control and help in monitoring and auditing. Supervisors and others with direct knowledge of how work is done can make important contributions to the preparation of procedures which will work in practice. Other examples of good co-operation include forming *ad hoc* problem-solving teams from different parts of the organisation to help solve specific problems - such as issues arising from an accident or a case of ill health. Such initiatives are supported by management and there is access to advice from health and safety specialists.

Opportunities to promote involvement also arise through the use of hazard report books, suggestion schemes or safety circles (similar to quality circles) where health and safety problems can be identified and solved. These too can develop enthusiasm and draw on worker expertise.

Yet organisations should recognise that involving employees may initially increase the potential for short-term conflict and disagreement about what constitutes safe and healthy working. They need to anticipate such conflict by supporting the activities of supervisors and managers with procedures which establish when and how specialist advice can be obtained to resolve problems and disputes. It may also be appropriate to identify when specific investigations are appropriate and any circumstances in which work should be suspended. The potential for conflict is likely to reduce in the longer term as participants develop more constructive working relationships and shared objectives.

Communication

Communication challenges organisations generally - not just on health and safety issues. It is often seen as the single most important area requiring improvement. The messages senior management wish to communicate are often not the ones employees receive. Two central elements are clear visible leadership and a common appreciation of how and why the organisation is trying to improve health and safety.

Effective communication about health and safety relies on information:

- coming **into** the organisation;
- flowing **within** the organisation;
- going **out** from the organisation.

Information inputs

Good sources of health and safety intelligence are as important in developing health and safety policy and performance as market information is for business development. Organisations need to monitor:

- legal developments to ensure they can comply with the law;
- technical developments relevant to risk control;
- developments in health and safety management practice.

Information flows within the organisation

If the health and safety policy is to be understood and consistently implemented, the following key information needs to be communicated effectively:

- the meaning and purpose of the policy;
- the vision, values and beliefs which underlie it;
- the commitment of senior management to its implementation;
- plans, standards, procedures and systems relating to implementation and measurement of performance;
- factual information to help secure the involvement and commitment of employees;
- comments and ideas for improvement;
- performance reports;
- lessons learned from accidents and other incidents.

Three interrelated methods can be used to provide an adequate flow of information up, down and across the organisation. They use both formal and informal means, but they need to be consistent with each other, especially where key messages can be reinforced by more than one method.

Visible behaviour

Managers, particularly senior managers, can communicate powerful signals about the importance and significance of health and safety objectives if they lead by example. Equally, they can undermine the development of a positive health and safety culture through negative behaviour. Subordinates soon recognise what their superiors regard as important and act accordingly. Successful methods which signal commitment include:

■ regular health and safety tours. These are not detailed inspections but a way of demonstrating management commitment and interest and to see obvious examples of good or bad performance. They can be planned to cover the whole site or operation progressively or to focus attention on current priorities in the overall safety effort;

■ chairing meetings of the central health and safety committee or joint consultative body;

■ active involvement in investigations of accidents, ill health and incidents. The level of seniority can be determined by the potential severity of the event.

Written communication

Among the most important written communications are:

■ health and safety policy statements;
■ organisation statements showing health and safety roles and responsibilities;
■ documented performance standards;
■ supporting organisational and risk control information and procedures;
■ significant findings from risk assessments.

In Chapter 2, examples were given of statements of philosophy. They showed how organisations try to make their values and beliefs explicit. The formal health and safety policy statement is a key written communication in any organisation. Specific details are required and an outline is shown in Inset 7.

Health and safety documentation needs to be tailored to the organisation's business needs, bearing in mind the requirements of specific legislation. In general the degree of detail should be proportionate to the level of complexity and the hazards and risks. The greater the risk, the more specific instructions need to be. In some cases, formal systems may be needed to keep track of key documentation but material should always be written according to the needs of the user.

Organisations can use notices, posters, handbills or health and safety newsletters to inform employees about particular issues or about progress in achieving objectives. These might include results of inspections, compliance with standards or the outcome of investigations. Well-directed use of notices or posters can support the achievement of specific targets or improve knowledge of particular risks. For this reason these things are likely to be more effective than general poster campaigns.

Face-to-face discussion

Opportunities for employees to have face-to-face discussion support other communication activities and enable them to make a more personal contribution. Tours and formal consultation meetings are options but others include:

■ planned meetings (or team briefings) at which information can be cascaded. These can include targeting particular groups of workers for safety critical tasks;

■ health and safety issues on the agenda at all routine management meetings (possibly as the first item);

■ monthly or weekly 'tool-box' talks or 'tailgate' meetings at which supervisors can discuss health and safety issues with their teams, remind them of critical risks and precautions and supplement the organisation's training effort. These also provide opportunities for employees to make their own suggestions (perhaps by 'brainstorming') about improving health and safety arrangements.

Inset 7 **An outline for statements of health and safety policy**

Written statements of health and safety policy should at the very least:

1   Set the **direction** for the organisation by:

■   demonstrating senior management commitment;

■   setting health and safety in context with other business objectives;

■   making a commitment to continuous improvement in health and safety performance.

2   Outline the **details** of the policy framework, showing how implementation will take place by:

■   identifying the Director or key Senior Manager with overall responsibility for formulating and implementing the policy;

■   having the document signed and dated by the Director or Chief Executive;

■   explaining the responsibilities of managers and staff;

■   recognising and encouraging the involvement of employees and safety representatives;

■   outlining the basis for effective communications;

■   showing how adequate resources will be allocated;

■   committing the leaders to planning and regularly reviewing and developing the policy;

■   securing the competence of all employees and the provision of any necessary specialist advice.

The policy provides the framework. Depending on the type of organisation and the risks involved, it may need to be supplemented by more detailed statements of organisation and the arrangements necessary to implement it.

Information flow from the organisation

Organisations may need to pass health and safety information to others, including:

- accident or ill health information to enforcing authorities;
- information about the safety of articles and substances supplied for use at work;
- emergency planning information.

The format for such information is sometimes specified in, for instance, an accident report form, a data sheet or a prescribed layout. It may be appropriate to seek professional advice on how to present less formal information so that it can be understood by the audience to whom it is addressed. Special arrangements may also be necessary for maintaining lines of communication whenever emergencies arise.

Competence

If all employees are to make a maximum contribution to health and safety, there must be proper arrangements in place to ensure that they are competent. This means more than simply training them. Experience of applying skills and knowledge is another important ingredient and needs to be gained under adequate supervision. Managers need to be aware of relevant legislation and how to manage health and safety effectively. All employees need to be able to work in a safe and healthy manner. It may also be necessary to examine the abilities of contractors where they work close to, or in collaboration with, direct employees. Good arrangements will include:

- recruitment and placement procedures which ensure that employees (including managers) have the necessary physical and mental abilities to do their jobs or can acquire them through training and experience. This may require assessments of individual fitness by medical examination and tests of physical fitness or aptitudes and abilities;
- systems to identify health and safety training needs arising from recruitment, changes in staff, plant, substances, technology, processes or working practices;
- the need to maintain or enhance competence by refresher training; and the presence of contractors' employees, self-employed people or temporary workers;
- systems and resources to provide the information, instruction, training and supporting communications effort to meet these needs;
- arrangements to ensure competent cover for staff absences, particularly those with critical health and safety responsibilities;
- general health promotion and surveillance schemes which contribute to the maintenance of general health and fitness (this may include assessments of fitness for work, rehabilitation, job adaptation following injury or ill health or a policy on drugs or alcohol).

Inset 8 provides further guidance on training. Proper supervision helps to ensure the development and maintenance of competence and is particularly necessary for those new to a job or undergoing training.

Inset 8 **Training for health and safety**

Training helps people acquire the skills, knowledge and attitudes to make them competent in the health and safety aspects of their work. It includes formal off-the-job training, instruction to individuals and groups, and on-the-job coaching and counselling.

But training is only one way of ensuring satisfactory health and safety performance. It is also helpful to integrate health and safety requirements into job specifications.

A typical training cycle is shown here.

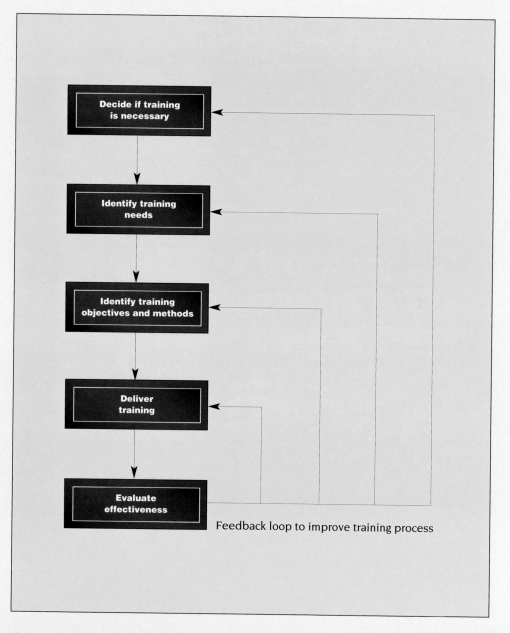

Diagram 5 A typical training cycle

continued overleaf

Inset 8 (continued)

Decide if training is necessary

Training should not be a substitute for proper risk control, for example to compensate for poorly designed plant or inadequate workstations. But it may be appropriate as a temporary means of control until improvements can be made. The key to effective training is to understand job requirements and individual abilities.

Identify training needs

Training needs can be identified by looking explicitly at the health and safety elements in individual jobs or tasks. For new jobs, a little imagination may be needed to compare them with existing jobs or to learn from other organisations doing similar work. For existing jobs, you can do the following things:

- consult job-specific accident, ill health and incident records to see what caused losses of control and how you can prevent them;
- gather information from employees about how the work is done;
- observe and question employees when they are working, to understand what they are doing and why. This may be particularly relevant in complex process plant where any analysis has to take account of all the possible consequences of human error, some of which may be remote from the particular task in hand. It could include formal task or error analysis;
- consult risk assessments for the work.

When you examine management jobs, your analysis also needs to consider the health and safety supervisory elements.

You can apply your analysis to complete jobs or subsidiary tasks. Complete analysis is essential for new starters but existing workers may need to improve performance on particular tasks.

These analyses need to be detailed and thorough. They may be resource intensive. But the benefits go beyond just training. They can influence other elements of the health and safety management system including:

- recruitment, selection and placement;
- the identification of critical tasks which need careful planning and monitoring;
- individual performance assessment;
- assessment of the suitability of an individual for promotion or substitution to a job where health and safety factors are important.

There are three main types of training need: organisational, job related and individual.

Inset 8 (*continued*)

Organisational needs

Everyone in the organisation needs to know about:

- the organisation's health and safety policy and the philosophy underlying it;
- the structure and systems for delivering the policy.

People will also need to know which parts of the systems are relevant to them, to understand the major risks in the organisation's activities and how they are controlled.

Job needs

These fall into two main types, management needs and non-management needs.

Management needs include:

- leadership skills;
- communication skills;
- techniques of health and safety management;
- training, instruction, coaching and problem-solving skills relevant to health and safety;
- understanding of the risks within a manager's area of responsibility;
- knowledge of relevant legislation and appropriate methods of control including risk assessment;
- knowledge of the organisation's planning, measuring, reviewing and auditing arrangements.

Some managers in key positions may have particular needs. This would apply to those who devise and develop the health and safety management system, investigate accidents or incidents, take part in review and audit activity or have to implement emergency procedures.

Non-management needs include:

- an overview of health and safety principles;
- detailed knowledge of the health and safety arrangements relevant to an individual's job;
- communication and problem-solving skills to encourage effective participation in health and safety activities.

Individual needs

Individual needs are generally identified through performance appraisal. They may also arise because an individual has not absorbed formal job training or information provided as part of their induction. Training needs vary over time, and assessments should cover:

- induction of new starters, including part-time and temporary workers;
- maintaining or updating the performance of established employees (especially if they may be involved in critical emergency procedures);

continued overleaf

Inset 8 (*continued*)

- ■ job changes, promotion or when someone has to deputise;
- ■ introduction of new equipment or technology;
- ■ follow-up action after an incident investigation.

Identify objectives and methods

Based on job analysis and risk assessment, you can set objectives and priorities. These can be used as the basis for measuring the effectiveness of training. You will need to devise training methods to suit the objectives. Some training needs may have to be met through closely supervised on-the-job experience. For some high-risk jobs and tasks the training may include simulation exercises. Distance-learning or computer-based interactive material may also be available.

Deliver training

Training can take place internally or externally, in either case using internal resources or consultants. Timing, cost and expertise generally determine the final choice.

Evaluation and feedback

You should formally evaluate training to see if it has led to the desired improvement in work performance and to help in targeting future training. Companies achieving high standards give high priority to systematic health and safety training.

National and Scottish Vocational Qualifications

National Vocational Qualifications (NVQs) and Scottish Vocational Qualifications (SVQs) are based on standards developed by Lead Bodies (LBs) (made up of representatives of employers, trade unions and professional groups). They identify standards of competence for particular occupations and the level of performance required to achieve them. NVQs and SVQs reflect not just the training given to individuals, but their ability to perform activities in an occupation to the standard expected at work.

For further guidance, see the HSE leaflet INDG345, *Health and safety training: What you need to know.*[16]

Competent employees and their representatives can make far more effective contributions to health and safety, whether as individuals or in groups, by participating actively in initiatives such as hazard spotting, problem solving and standards improvement. But, even though managers, supervisors and other employees can achieve high levels of competence, there may still be a need for professional health and safety advice from within the organisation or outside. The roles and functions of health and safety advisers are outlined in Inset 9.

Inset 9 **Role and functions of health and safety advisers**

Health and safety advisers need to have the **status** and **competence** to advise management and employees or their representatives with authority and independence. They are well placed to advise on:

■ formulating and developing health and safety policies, not just for existing activities but also with respect to new acquisitions or processes;

■ how organisations can promote a positive health and safety culture and secure the effective implementation of health and safety policy;

■ planning for health and safety including the setting of realistic short- and long-term objectives, deciding priorities and establishing adequate systems and performance standards;

■ day-to-day implementation and monitoring of policy and plans including accident and incident investigation, reporting and analysis;

■ review of performance and audit of the whole health and safety management system.

To do this properly, health and safety advisers need to:

■ be properly trained and suitably qualified; (the Health and Safety National Occupational standards[17] offer one route to demonstrating competence);

■ maintain adequate information systems on topics including civil and criminal law, health and safety management and technical advances;

■ interpret the law in the context of their own organisation;

■ be involved in establishing organisational arrangements, systems and risk control standards relating to hardware and human performance, by advising line management on matters such as legal and technical standards;

■ establish and maintain procedures for reporting, investigating, recording and analysing accidents and incidents;

■ establish and maintain procedures, including monitoring and other means such as review and auditing, to ensure senior managers get a true picture of how well health and safety is being managed (where a benchmarking role may be especially valuable);

■ present their advice independently and effectively.

Relationships within the organisation

Health and safety advisers:

■ support the provision of authoritative and independent advice;

■ have a direct reporting line to directors on matters of policy and the authority to stop work if it contravenes agreed standards and puts people at risk of injury;

■ have responsibility for professional standards and systems. On large sites or in a group of companies, they may also have line management responsibility for other health and safety professionals.

continued overleaf

Inset 9 (*continued*)

Relationships outside the organisation

Health and safety advisers liaise with a wide range of bodies and individuals including: local authority environmental health officers and licensing officials, architects and consultants, the Fire Service, contractors, insurance companies, clients and customers, HSE, the public, equipment suppliers, HM Coroner or the Procurator Fiscal, the media, the police, general practitioners, and occupational health specialists and services.

CHAPTER FOUR

Planning and implementing

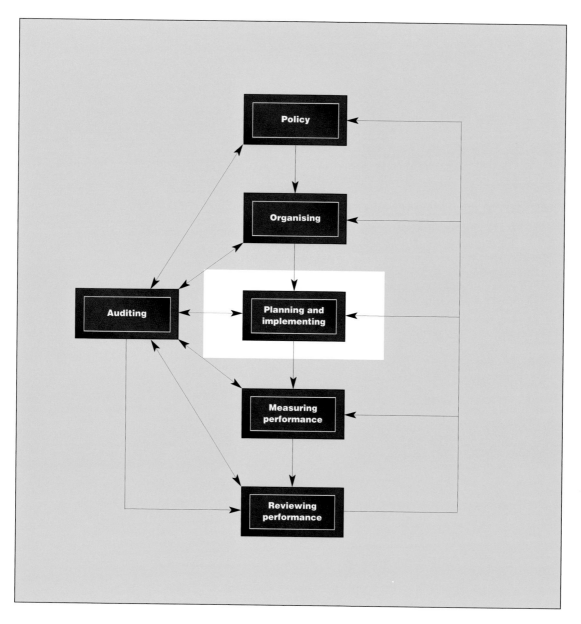

KEY MESSAGES

Planning is essential for the implementation of health and safety policies. Adequate control of risks can only be achieved through co-ordinated action by all members of the organisation. An effective planning system for health and safety requires organisations to establish and operate a health and safety management system which:

controls risks;

reacts to changing demands;

sustains a positive health and safety culture.

Planning for health and safety

The results of successful health and safety management are often expressed as a series of negative outcomes, such as an absence of injuries, ill health, incidents or losses. But it is often a matter of chance whether dangerous events cause injury or loss (see Inset 1). Effective planning is concerned with prevention through identifying, eliminating and controlling hazards and risks. This is especially important when dealing with health risks which may only become apparent after a long latency period.

Prevention can only stem from an effective health and safety management system, and organisations need a framework or benchmark against which to judge the adequacy of the current situation. Although health and safety management systems vary in detail they have some general characteristics described here.

Workplace precautions

The ultimate goal of any health and safety management system is to prevent injury and ill health in the workplace. Adequate workplace precautions have to be provided and maintained to prevent harm to people at the point of risk. Risks are created in the business process as resources and information are used to create products and services (see Diagram 6). Workplace precautions to match the hazards and risks are needed at each stage of business activity. They can include machine guards, local exhaust ventilation, safety instructions and systems of work.

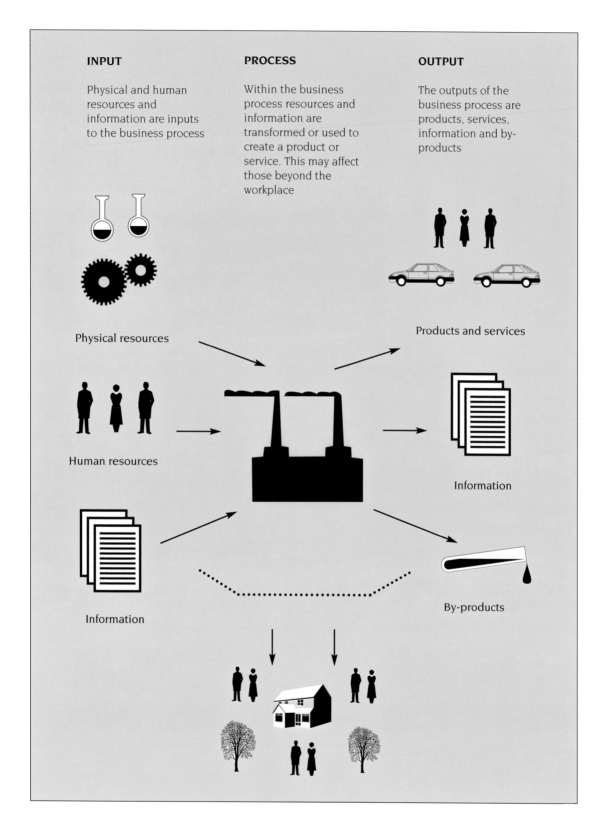

INPUT

Physical and human resources and information are inputs to the business process

PROCESS

Within the business process resources and information are transformed or used to create a product or service. This may affect those beyond the workplace

OUTPUT

The outputs of the business process are products, services, information and by-products

Physical resources

Human resources

Information

Products and services

Information

By-products

Diagram 6 *The business process* (Workplace precautions are needed at each stage)

This shows a manufacturing unit but the model also applies to other industries including construction, mines, universities, hospitals and local authorities.

Risk control systems (RCSs)

Risk control systems are the basis for ensuring that adequate workplace precautions are provided and maintained. Diagram 7 shows a typical range of activities for which risk control systems may be needed.

INPUT	PROCESS	OUTPUT
Design/construction	Routine and non-routine operations	Product and service design
Design/installation	Maintenance	Packaging/labelling
Purchasing/procurement	Plant and process change	Storage/transport
Recruitment/selection	Foreseeable emergencies	Off-site risks
Selection of contractors	Decommission	Disposal and pollution control
Acquisitions	Demolition	Divestments
Information		Information

Diagram 7 *Risk control systems*

At the **input stage**, the aim is to minimise hazards and risks entering the organisation. At the **process stage**, the focus is on containing risks associated with the process. At the **output stage,** the RCSs should prevent the export of risks off-site, or in the products and services generated by the business.

The activities in Diagram 7 are typical of those found in many organisations but this is not a definitive list. RCSs are needed for them. The nature and relative importance of RCSs will vary according to the nature and hazard profile of the business and the workplace precautions. For instance:

- Organisations relying on significant numbers of contractors will need an effective RCS to select and control contractors.
- Wherever the containment of hazardous materials is important (eg where flammables or toxics are used), maintenance and process change procedures are necessary to ensure plant integrity.
- Organisations supplying materials or substances for others to use will focus on specific output issues such as storage, transport, packaging and labelling.

Organisations need RCSs which are appropriate to the hazards arising from their activities and sufficient to cover all hazards. The design, reliability and complexity of each RCS needs to be proportionate to the particular hazards and risks.

Management arrangements

A set of management processes is necessary to organise, plan, control and monitor the design and implementation of the RCSs. These are the key elements of health and safety management which are described in this guidance. Here they are summarised as 'management arrangements' (see Diagram 8).

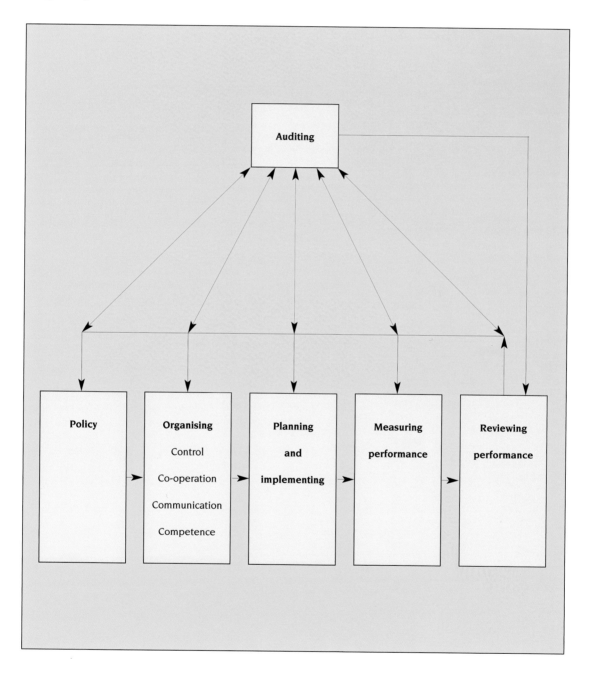

Diagram 8 *Management arrangements*

The three components can be assembled into a single 'picture' of a health and safety management system (see Diagram 9) which can form a framework for planning and auditing.

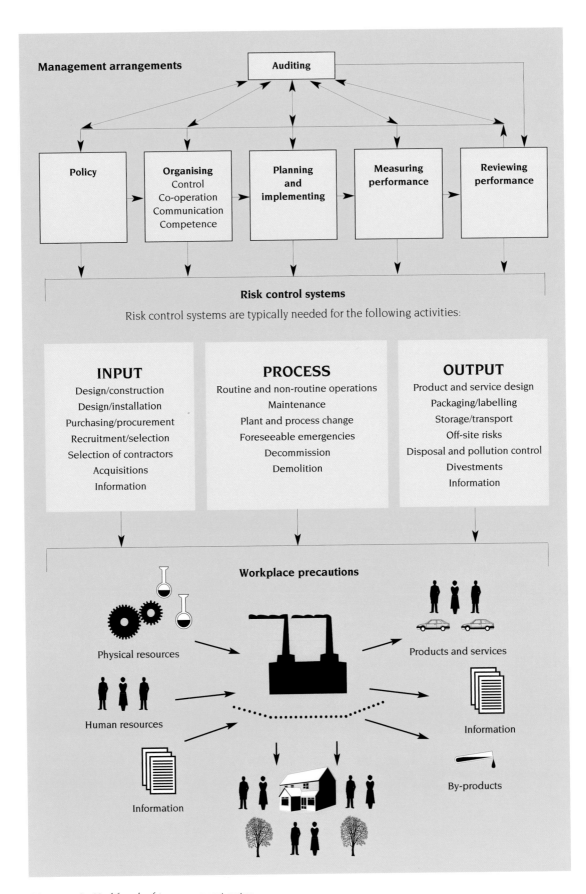

Diagram 9 *Health and safety management system*

This three-component framework can be applied to any organisation. In multi-site businesses, there need to be sufficient management arrangements at the centre to control and ensure that an adequate health and safety management system is provided at each business unit and site. The centre may wish to establish minimum expectations for management arrangements, RCSs and workplace precautions at each business unit and site.

Planning the overall health and safety management system

Organisations have to build an effective health and safety management system. They need to plan **how** to deal with each of the three 'components' in Diagram 9 and to **co-ordinate** the different activities at each level. Planning how to create and operate a health and safety management system ought to be a collaborative effort involving people throughout the organisation. It can also be a good way of demonstrating and gaining commitment to continuous improvement and promoting a health and safety culture.

Planning a health and safety management system involves:

■ designing, developing and installing suitable management arrangements, RCSs and workplace precautions which are proportionate to the needs, hazards and risks of the organisation; and

■ operating, maintaining and improving the system to suit changing needs and process hazards/risks.

A systematic approach is necessary to answer three key questions:

■ Where are we now?
■ Where do we want to be?
■ How do we get there?

These questions may need to be asked at all levels or parts of an organisation, depending on the size and complexity of the business. For instance, the answers will be different at the centre of a large multi-site organisation from those at an individual site. Planning has to be co-ordinated to ensure consistent implementation of policy, avoid duplication of effort and avoid critical omissions.

An effective planning process (see Diagram 10) comprises three elements:

■ accurate information about the current situation;
■ suitable benchmarks against which to make comparisons;
■ competent people to carry out the analysis and make judgements.

Input

Information on current conditions or status

Suitable benchmarks and legal standards

Competent people

Process

Where are we now? → **Where do we want to be?** → **How do we get there?**

Comparison with frameworks and legal standards

■ Is the system adequate? (Doing the right things)

■ Is the system working as intended? (Doing things right)

■ And is this resulting in cost-effective, proportionate prevention at the workplace?

'Gap' analysis leading to:

■ devising new components of the health and safety management system or

■ improving existing components

Output

Health and safety plans with objectives for developing, maintaining and improving the health and safety management system

Specifications for management arrangements, RCSs and workplace precautions

Performance standards for implementing the health and safety management system

Diagram 10 *Summary of the planning process*

To answer the question 'Where are we now?', an organisation has to compare the current situation against **both** the health and safety management framework described earlier (Diagram 9) and specific legal requirements. This analysis provides a view of the current state of the health and safety management system. Further judgement may be necessary to establish if the system is:

- adequate for the organisation and the range of hazards/risks;
- working as intended and achieving the right objectives; and
- delivering cost-effective and proportionate risk control in the workplace.

Deciding 'where we want to be?' is partly determined by the law. The simplest objective will always be to achieve legal compliance. Some organisations may, however, strive for higher standards and this will shape the way they build their management system. They may wish, for example, to be an industry leader in health and safety and its management.

Deciding 'how do we get there?' involves practical decisions about how to move forward. For example, organisations might decide to devise new components of the health and safety management system or to improve existing ones. They may use risk assessment to help them make decisions about improving workplace precautions. They also have to make decisions about the design of RCSs and management arrangements. Advice on devising RCSs and risk assessment is provided later in this chapter.

It may not be feasible to do all these jobs at once. An overall plan is usually necessary, setting out what is to be achieved in what timescale. This will depend on what resources are available and the starting point. To achieve world-class performance may take some time. Careful decisions over priorities will be needed. In general, emphasis should be given to providing comprehensive and adequate workplace precautions and RCSs which meet minimum legal requirements. Within this framework the emphasis should be on high hazard/risk activities. If fundamental changes cannot be made right away or within a reasonable time, then short-term measures should be taken to minimise risks.

There are three complementary outputs from the planning process:

- health and safety plans with objectives for developing, maintaining and improving the health and safety management system, such as:
  - requiring each site of a multi-site firm to have an annual health and safety plan and an accident and incident investigation system (to meet specific standards);
  - establishing a reliable risk assessment process for COSHH;
  - involving employees in preparing workplace precautions;
  - completing all manual handling assessments by the end of the current year;
  - providing a new guard for a particular machine;
- specifications for management arrangements, RCSs and workplace precautions; and

■ performance standards for implementing the health and safety management system, identifying the contribution of individuals to implementing the system (this is essential to building a positive health and safety culture).

Setting objectives

Health and safety objectives need to be specific, measurable, agreed with those who deliver them, realistic and set against a suitable timescale (SMART). Both short- and long-term objectives should be set and prioritised against business needs (advice on prioritising is given later in this chapter). Objectives at different levels or within different parts of an organisation should be aligned so they support the overall policy objectives. Personal targets can also be agreed with individuals to secure the attainment of objectives.

If initial diagnosis reveals a poorly developed system, the early emphasis will probably be on training people so that an improved health and safety planning process can be established as a basis for further development. Early decisions about the adequacy of workplace precautions and compliance with the law will also be necessary. As a foundation of competence is established, a sound health and safety planning and risk assessment process should emerge which will lead to improved control over significant risks. As improved control is established, the emphasis can shift to devising more comprehensive risk control systems and more effective management arrangements to establish a complete health and safety management system. As the specific components of the system are established and embedded, the emphasis can shift again to maintaining and developing the system to ensure there are no gaps or weaknesses and to consolidate the health and safety culture. The foundation has now been laid for a programme of continuous improvement.

Devising workplace precautions

The control of risks is necessary to secure compliance with the requirements of the HSW Act and the relevant statutory provisions. There are three basic stages in establishing workplace precautions:

■ **hazard identification** - identifying hazards which could cause harm;
■ **risk assessment** - assessing the risk which may arise from hazards;
■ **risk control** - deciding on suitable measures to eliminate or control risk.

This approach applies both to the control of health risks and safety risks. Health risks do, however, present distinctive features which require a particular approach. Inset 10 provides further details. The approach underpins legislation which aims to improve the management of health and safety, eg the Management of Health and Safety at Work Regulations 1999 (MHSW Regulations),[18] and the Control of Substances Hazardous to Health (COSHH) Regulations 2002 (as amended).[19]

Inset 10 **Controlling health risks**

Health and safety at work law places a duty on employers to ensure the health as well as the safety of their employees. The principles for controlling health through risk assessment are the same as those for safety. However, the nature of health risks can make the link between work activities and employee ill health less apparent than in the case of injury from an accident.

Unlike safety risks, which can lead to immediate injury, the results of daily exposure to health risks may not become apparent for months, years and in some cases, decades. Health may be irreversibly damaged before the risk is apparent. It is therefore essential to develop a preventive strategy to identify and control risks before anyone is exposed to them. Failure to do so can lead to workers' disability and loss of livelihood. It can also mean financial losses for the organisation through sickness absence, lost production, compensation and increased insurance premiums.

Risks to health from work activities include:

- skin contact with irritant substances, leading to dermatitis etc;
- inhalation of respiratory sensitisers, triggering immune responses such as asthma;
- badly designed workstations requiring awkward body postures or repetitive movements, resulting in upper limb disorders, repetitive strain injury and other musculoskeletal conditions;
- noise levels which are too high, causing deafness and conditions such as tinnitus;
- too much vibration, eg from hand-held tools leading to hand-arm vibration syndrome and circulatory problems;
- exposure to ionising and non-ionising radiation including ultraviolet in the sun's rays, causing burns, sickness and skin cancer;
- infections ranging from minor sickness to life-threatening conditions, caused by inhaling or being contaminated by micro-biological organisms;
- stress causing mental and physical disorders.

Some illnesses or conditions such as asthma and back pain have both occupational and non-occupational causes and it may be difficult to establish a definite link with a work activity or exposure to particular agents or substances. But, if there is information which shows that the illness or condition is prevalent among the occupational group to which the sufferers belong or among workers exposed to similar agents or substances, it is likely that their work is at least a contributory factor.

Some aspects of managing risks to health will need input from specialist or professional advisers such as technical staff or occupational health hygienists, nurses and doctors. There is much that can be done to prevent or control risks to health by taking straightforward measures such as:

- consulting the workforce on the design of workstations;
- talking to suppliers of substances, plant and equipment about minimising exposure;
- enclosing machinery to cut down noise;
- researching the use of less hazardous materials;
- ensuring that employees are trained in the safe handling of all the substances and materials with which they come into contact.

continued overleaf

Inset 10 (*continued*)

To assess health risks and to make sure that control measures are working properly, you may need for example to measure the concentration of substances in air to make sure that exposures remain within relevant maximum exposure limits or occupational exposure standards. Sometimes surveillance of workers at risk of exposure will be needed. This will enable data to be collected for the evaluation of controls and for early detection of adverse changes to health. Health surveillance procedures available include biological monitoring for bodily uptake of substances, examination for symptoms and medical surveillance - which may entail clinical examinations and physiological or psychological measurements. The procedure chosen should be suitable for the case concerned. Sometimes a method of surveillance is specified for a particular substance, for example, in the COSHH Approved Code of Practice. Whenever surveillance is undertaken, a health record has to be kept for the person concerned.

Health surveillance should be supervised by a registered medical practitioner or, where appropriate, it should be done by a suitably qualified person (eg an occupational nurse). In the case of inspections for easily detectable symptoms like chrome ulceration or early signs of dermatitis, health surveillance should be done by a suitably trained responsible person. If workers could be exposed to substances listed in Schedule 6 of COSHH, medical surveillance under the supervision of an HSE employment medical adviser or a doctor appointed by HSE is required.

Although, as described, specialist help may be needed to control risks to health, employers themselves remain responsible for managing work activities in a way that will prevent employees being made ill by their work.

For more information, see *Health risk management: A practical guide for managers in small and medium-sized enterprises.*[20]

In practice many decisions at these three stages are simple and straightforward and are taken together. Wherever the identification stage reveals a well-known hazard with a known risk, the methods of control and consequent maintenance may be well tried and tested. For example, stairs present an established risk of slipping, tripping and falling. They require traditional methods of control such as good construction, the use of handrails and the provision of non-slip surfaces along with the need to keep stairs free of obstructions. In other more complex situations decisions are necessary at each stage. These are outlined below.

Hazard identification

The essential first step in risk control is to seek out and identify hazards. Relevant sources of information include:

■   legislation and supporting Approved Codes of Practice which give practical guidance
     and include basic minimum requirements;

- HSE guidance;
- process information;
- product information provided under section 6 of the HSW Act;
- relevant British and international standards;
- industry or trade association guidance;
- the personal knowledge and experience of managers and employees;
- accident, ill health and incident data from within the organisation, from other organisations or from central sources;
- expert advice and opinion and relevant research.

There should be a critical appraisal of all routine and non-routine business activities. People exposed may include not just employees, but also others such as members of the public, contractors and users of the products and services. Employees and safety representatives can make a useful contribution in identifying hazards.

In the simplest cases, hazards can be identified by observation and by comparing the circumstances with the relevant information (eg single-storey premises will not present any hazards associated with stairs). In more complex cases, measurements such as air sampling or examining the methods of machine operation may be necessary to identify the presence of hazards from chemicals or machinery. In the most complex or high-risk cases (for example, in the chemical or nuclear industry) special techniques and systems may be needed such as hazard and operability studies (HAZOPS) and hazard analysis techniques such as event or fault-tree analysis. Specialist advice may be needed to choose and apply the most appropriate method.

Risk assessment

There is a general requirement to carry out risk assessment under the MHSW Regulations 1999. (Guidance is given in the HSE leaflet 5 *steps to risk assessment* INDG163.[21])

Assessing risks to help determine workplace precautions can be qualitative or quantitative. In the simplest cases, you can refer to specific legal limits; for example, people are liable to fall a distance of 2 m from an open edge or they are not. In more complex situations, you may need to make qualitative judgements within a framework set by legal standards and guidance. The Control of Substances Hazardous to Health Regulations 2002 (COSHH) and the accompanying Approved Code of Practice establish a decision-making framework if hazardous substances are used. Quantitative risk assessment (QRA) techniques may be used as a basis for making decisions in more complex industries. QRA is specifically referred to in the Offshore Installations (Safety Case) Regulations 1992.[22]

To assess risks, you need a similar knowledge of activities and working practices as to conduct hazard identification. Again, the knowledge of employees and safety representatives can prove valuable. Risk assessments should be done by competent people. Professional health and safety advice may be needed in some cases, especially when choosing appropriate QRA techniques and interpreting results.

Risk control

When risks have been analysed and assessed, you can make decisions about workplace precautions.

All final decisions about risk control methods must take into account the relevant legal requirements which establish minimum levels of risk prevention or control. Some of the duties imposed by the HSW Act and the relevant statutory provisions are absolute and must be complied with. Many requirements are, however, qualified by the words, **'so far as is reasonably practicable'**, or **'so far as is practicable'**. These require an assessment of cost, along with information about relative costs, effectiveness and reliability of different control measures. Other duties require the use of **'best practicable means'** - often used in the context of controlling sources of environmental pollution such as emissions to the atmosphere. Further guidance on the meaning of these three expressions is provided in Inset 11.

Inset 11

'So far as is reasonably practicable', 'So far as is practicable', and 'Best practicable means'

Although none of these expressions are defined in the HSW Act, they have acquired meanings through many interpretations by the courts and it is the courts which, in the final analysis, decide their application in particular cases.

To carry out a duty **so far as is reasonably practicable** means that the degree of risk in a particular activity or environment can be balanced against the time, trouble, cost and physical difficulty of taking measures to avoid the risk. If these are so disproportionate to the risk that it would be unreasonable for the people concerned to have to incur them to prevent it, they are not obliged to do so. The greater the risk, the more likely it is that it is reasonable to go to very substantial expense, trouble and invention to reduce it. But if the consequences and the extent of a risk are small, insistence on great expense would not be considered reasonable. It is important to remember that the judgement is an objective one and the size or financial position of the employer are immaterial.

So far as is practicable, without the qualifying word 'reasonably', implies a stricter standard. This term generally embraces whatever is technically possible in the light of current knowledge, which the person concerned had or ought to have had at the time. The cost, time and trouble involved are not to be taken into account.

The meaning of **best practicable means** can vary depending on its context and ultimately it is for the courts to decide. Where the law prescribes that 'best practicable means' should be employed, it is usual for the regulating authority to indicate its view of what is practicable in notes or even agreements with particular firms or industries. Both these notes or agreements and the views likely to be taken by a court will be influenced by considerations of cost and technical practicability. But the view generally adopted by HSE inspectors is that an element of reasonableness is involved in considering whether the best practicable means had been used in a particular situation.

Where legal requirements demand an assessment of cost, information about the relative costs, effectiveness and reliability of different control measures will be needed to make decisions about acceptable levels of control.

Decisions about the reliability of controls can be guided by reference to the preferred hierarchy of control which has now been incorporated into regulations such as MHSW and COSHH. The following is a summary of the preferred hierarchy of risk control principles:

■ **Eliminate risks** by substituting the dangerous by the inherently less dangerous, eg:

▨ use less hazardous substances;

▨ substitute a type of machine which is better guarded to make the same product;

▨ avoid the use of certain processes, eg by buying from subcontractors.

■ **Combat risks** at source by engineering controls and giving collective protective measures priority, eg:

▨ separate the operator from the risk of exposure to a known hazardous substance by enclosing the process;

▨ protect the dangerous parts of a machine by guarding;

▨ design process machinery and work activities to minimise the release, or to suppress or contain airborne hazards;

▨ design machinery which is remotely operated and to which materials are fed automatically, thus separating the operator from danger areas.

■ **Minimise risk** by:

▨ designing suitable systems of working;

▨ using personal protective clothing and equipment; this should only be used as a last resort.

The hierarchy reflects the fact that eliminating and controlling risk by using physical engineering controls and safeguards is more reliable than relying solely on people.

If a range of precautions is available, the relative costs need to be weighed against the degree of control provided, both in the short and long term. Some control measures, such as eliminating a risk by choosing a safer alternative substance or machine, provide a high degree of control and are reliable. However, physical safeguards such as guarding a machine or enclosing a hazardous process need to be maintained and this imposes an extra longer-term cost.

The design of all workplace precautions should consider the human factors outlined in Inset 2. In successful organisations the design of precautions is fully integrated into plant and work design procedures so that specifications simultaneously satisfy output, quality, and health and safety requirements. Employee involvement encourages solutions which are relevant and practical for those who have to implement them.

Devising risk control systems (RCSs)

The purpose of RCSs is to make sure that appropriate workplace precautions are implemented and kept in place. HSE experience suggests that organisations often place insufficient emphasis on this aspect of their health and safety system. The control systems should reflect the hazard profile of the organisation; the greater the hazard or risk, the more robust and reliable the control systems need to be. Inset 12 provides a framework for deciding which RCSs are necessary.

The planning of RCSs requires decisions on what control systems are necessary, and their design. The basic elements of policy, organising, implementing, measuring, reviewing and auditing can be used as a framework for designing the systems. This defines a management control loop (Plan-Do-Check-Act). A practical example of how this can be applied is shown below for a permit-to-work system:

Policy

- What is the purpose and objective of the permit-to-work system and what are its scope and limitations? For example, the purpose of the permit-to-work system is to establish control over high-risk maintenance or other unusual work.

Organising

- Control - who will be responsible for operating and running the system? For example, who will devise and design the system? Who will implement it? Who will monitor and review performance and audit its operation?

- Co-operation - how will system users be involved in its development to ensure its acceptance and effective working? How will deficiencies and weaknesses and failings in the system be reported?

- Communication - what communication is necessary to ensure the effective operation of the system and between the various parties issuing and using a permit? What documentation is involved and how can it be designed to be clear, effective and simple to use?

- Competence - what training, qualifications, skills and level of competence are required for:
- those issuing permits?
- those doing work under permits?
- those monitoring, reviewing performance etc?

Implementing

- What workplace precautions are necessary for each type of permit? What are the rules of the system and how does it work? Are the rules simple so that they can always be easily applied? Are there sufficient resources to ensure that the system can be applied in full? What are the performance standards for the various individuals involved - who does what, when, and how (see Inset 5)?

Measuring performance

■ How will the implementation and effectiveness of the system be measured? For example, will there be a periodic inspection of the work activity and of a sample of permits to ensure proper completion and effective use?

Reviewing performance

■ How will the findings from the measuring activities be used to review and improve the system?

Auditing

■ How will the system be independently audited and verified?

Inset 12 **Framework for setting risk control systems**

This inset states in general terms the range of possible activities for which RCSs may be needed. The RCSs should match the hazard profile of the business; more resources will be necessary for the more significant hazards.

First stage controls

Control of inputs

Objective: To minimise hazards entering the organisation.

RCSs are needed to control the flows of resources and information through the organisation. At the **input stage** the goal is to eliminate and minimise hazards and risks entering the organisation. RCSs may be needed for:

■ **physical resources** including:
▨ the design, selection, purchase and construction of workplaces;
▨ the design, selection, purchase and installation of plant and substances used by the organisation;
▨ the plant and substances used by others, such as contractors on site;
▨ the acquisition of new businesses;

■ **human resources** including:
▨ the recruitment and selection of all employees;
▨ the selection of contracting organisations;

■ **information** including:
▨ information relating directly to health and safety, such as standards, guidance and aspects of the law, and any revisions;
▨ other technical and management information relating to risk control and the development of a positive health and safety culture.

continued overleaf

Inset 12 (*continued*)

Second stage controls

Control of work activities

Objective: To eliminate and minimise risks within the business process.

At the process stage, hazards are created where people interact with their jobs, and the goal is to eliminate or minimise risks arising inside the organisation. RCSs may need to cover the four areas concerned with work activities and risk creation, namely:

■ **premises** - including the place of work, entrances and exits, the general working environment, welfare facilities, and all plant and facilities which are part of the fixed structure, such as permanent electrical installations;

■ **plant and substances** - including the arrangements for their handling, transport, storage and use;

■ **procedures** - including the design of jobs and work procedures and all aspects of the way the work is done;

■ **people** - including the placement of employees, their competence for the job and any health surveillance needed.

When specifying RCSs it is necessary in each case to consider:

■ the operation of the business process in the 'steady state', including routine and non-routine activities;

■ the business process in the 'steady state' during maintenance, including the maintenance activity itself, whether undertaken by contractors or on-site staff;

■ planned changes from the 'steady state', arising from any change in the organisation structure, premises, plant, process, substances, procedures, people or information;

■ foreseeable emergencies giving rise to serious and imminent danger, such as fire, injuries, ill health, incidents or the failure of control equipment (including first aid, emergency planning and procedures for the management of emergencies, and identification and control of danger areas);

■ decommissioning, dismantling and removal of facilities, plant, equipment or substances.

Third stage controls

Control of outputs

Objective: To minimise risks outside the organisation arising from the business process, products and services.

Inset 12 (*continued*)

At the **output stage** the goal is to minimise the risks to people outside the organisation whether from work activities themselves or from the products or services supplied. RCSs may need to cover:

- products and services, and include consideration of:
- design and research on the health and safety and safe use of products and services, including surveillance of users to identify evidence of harm;
- the delivery and transport of products including packaging, labelling and intermediate storage;
- the installation, setting up, cleaning and maintenance of products undertaken by employees or contractors;

- by-products of the work activities, such as:
- off-site risks which might arise from the organisation's work activities both at fixed or transient sites;
- outputs to the environment - particularly wastes and atmospheric emissions;
- the disposal of plant, equipment and substances (including wastes);

- information, for example:
- the health and safety information provided to those transporting, handling, storing, purchasing, using or disposing of products;
- the information provided to those who may be affected by work activities, such as members of the public, other employers and their employees, the emergency services and planning authorities.

Devising management arrangements

The framework in this guidance provides a basis for making judgements on how to design management arrangements to suit an organisation. The scope and complexity of the management arrangements should reflect the business needs and hazard profile. What is suitable for a large multi-site organisation will not be appropriate for a small firm, but there needs to be appropriate activity across all six key elements of the framework (policy, organising, planning and implementing, measuring performance, review and audit).

Setting performance standards

Performance standards are needed to identify the contribution that people make to operating the health and safety management system.

Standards for people at all levels are needed to ensure:

- the effective design, development and installation of the health and safety management system;

- the consistent implementation and improvement of the health and safety management system, ie the management arrangements, RCSs and workplace precautions; and

- that positive rewards can be provided for individuals in recognition of the effort put into accident and ill health prevention.

Performance standards are the foundation for a positive health and safety culture. The format of standards was considered earlier (see Inset 5). At the planning stage, decisions are needed about the appropriate standards to match the needs of the business and the health and safety management system. Performance standards could cover the following:

- policy formulation and development;
- methods of accountability;
- health and safety committee and similar consultation meetings;
- involvement of people in risk assessments and writing procedures;
- collection and dissemination of information from external sources;
- the involvement of senior managers in safety tours and accident and incident investigations;
- preparation of health and safety documentation, performance standards, rules and procedures;
- health and safety plans and objectives;
- the risk assessment process;
- implementation of RCSs and workplace precautions;
- the active monitoring arrangements including inspections;
- the accident and incident reporting and investigation system;
- audit and review.

Prioritising health and safety activities

Systems of assessing relative hazard and risk can contribute to decisions about priorities. They are also a useful aid to answering questions of importance and urgency arising at other stages in planning and implementing a health and safety management system, for example:

- prioritising different health and safety objectives;
- deciding on the hazard profile of the business to reveal those areas where more robust and reliable workplace precautions and RCSs will be needed;
- deciding monitoring priorities;
- establishing priorities for training and improving levels of competence;
- what, if any, immediate action is needed to prevent further injury following an accident;
- what, if any, immediate action is necessary to prevent injury following an incident or the discovery of a hazard;
- when reviewing the results of monitoring activities and the results of injury, ill health and incident investigations;
- deciding the extent of the resources needed and the speed of the response which should be made following a particular accident or incident.

While there is no general formula for rating hazards and risks, several techniques can help in decision-making. **These differ from the detailed risk assessments needed to establish workplace precautions to satisfy legal standards**. The techniques involve a means of ranking hazards and risks. Some systems rank hazards, others rank risks. Assessing relative risk involves some means of estimating the likelihood of occurrence and the severity of a hazard. A simple form of risk estimation is described below to illustrate the general principles.

Simple risk estimation

Hazard - the potential to cause harm will vary in severity. The likely effect of a hazard may, for example be rated:

Major
Death or major injury (as defined in RIDDOR[23]) or illness causing long-term disability.

Serious
Injuries or illness causing short-term disability.

Slight
All other injuries or illness.

Harm may not arise from exposure to a hazard in every case. In practice the likelihood and severity of harm will be affected by how the work is organised, how effectively the hazard is controlled, and the extent and nature of exposure to it. In the case of health risks, the latent effects and the susceptibility of individuals will also be relevant. Judgements about likelihood will also be affected by experience of working with a hazard; for example, the analysis of accident, ill health and incident data may provide a clue. The likelihood of harm may be rated:

High
Where it is certain or near certain that harm will occur.

Medium
Where harm will often occur.

Low
Where harm will seldom occur.

In this case risk can be defined as the combination of the severity of harm with the likelihood of its occurrence, or:

Risk = Severity x Likelihood of
of harm   occurrence

This simple computation enables a rough and ready comparison of risks. If hazards could affect more than one person you could assign a relative weighting to reflect this.

This example presents the most simplified method of estimating relative risk. In practice, organisations need to use systems suited to their own needs. Hazard rating systems have been developed by Dow[24] and ICI (the Mond Index).

Implementing the health and safety management system

If workplace precautions, RCSs and management arrangements are well designed and recognise existing business practice and human capabilities and fallibilities, they will be easier to implement. Adequate documentation can also contribute to consistent application. In some cases the law requires suitable records to be maintained (eg a record of risk assessments under the MHSW Regulations[18] and COSHH[19]). Safety case regulations covering offshore installations[22] and railways[25] require you to keep more detailed records of process hazards, risks and precautions.

You should document other health and safety system information so that it is proportionate to business needs, hazards and risks. The control of relatively minor hazards affecting all employees (such as ensuring passages and gangways remain free from obstruction) can be dealt with by a number of simply stated general rules. The control of more hazardous activities may need more detailed workplace precautions and RCSs. The control of high hazard activities may demand detailed workplace precautions and an RCS which needs to be strictly followed, such as a permit-to-work system.

All the components of the health and safety management system need to be adequately inspected, maintained and monitored to secure continued effective operation. Risk assessments and workplace precautions should be reviewed in the light of changes and technological developments. The type, frequency and depth of maintenance should reflect the extent and nature of the hazard and risks revealed by risk assessment. The balance of resources devoted to the various RCSs will also reflect the hazard profile of the business.

For a summary of recent research by HSE into the experiences of organisations that have implemented new management systems, see Appendix 4.

Even in a well-designed and well-developed health and safety management system there is still the challenge of ensuring that all requirements are complied with consistently. The main way of achieving this is by rewarding positive behaviour according to the maxim of 'what gets rewarded gets done'.

After an accident or case of ill health, many organisations find that they **already** had systems, rules, procedures or instructions which would have prevented the event but which were not complied with. There are many reasons why such 'violations' occur. The underlying causes often lie in systems which are designed without taking proper account of human factors, or violations are condoned implicitly or explicitly by management action or neglect (see *Reducing error and influencing behaviour*[3], and *Improving compliance with safety procedures: Reducing industrial violations*[26]). Managers need to take positive steps to address human factors issues and to encourage safe behaviour. They need to recognise that the prevailing health and safety culture is a major influence in shaping people's safety-related behaviour.[11]

Some organisations have applied performance management techniques and behaviour modification to promote and reward safe behaviour and reduce unsafe behaviour.[28,29] Such techniques can play an important part in accident and ill health prevention and promoting a positive health and safety culture. However, they are no substitute for a sound health and safety management system. They achieve their best effect where the health and safety system is relatively well developed and where employees are actively involved in the behavioural safety process.

CHAPTER FIVE

Measuring performance

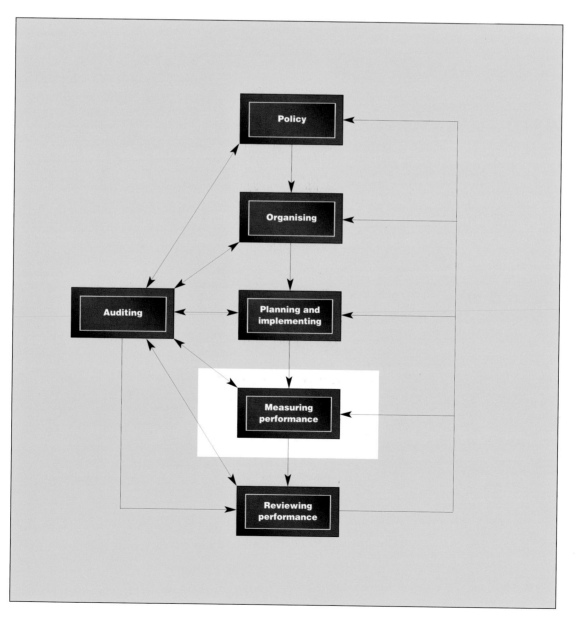

KEY MESSAGES

Measurement is essential to maintain and improve health and safety performance. There are two ways to generate information on performance:

active systems which monitor the achievement of plans and the extent of compliance with standards;

reactive systems which monitor accidents, ill health and incidents.

Effective procedures are needed to capture both sorts of information.

Organisations need to measure what they are doing to implement their health and safety policy, to assess how effectively they are controlling risks, and how well they are developing a positive health and safety culture. A low accident rate, even over a period of years, is no guarantee that risks are being effectively controlled and will not lead to injuries, ill health or loss in the future. This is particularly true in organisations where there is a low probability of accidents but where major hazards are present. Here the historical record can be an unreliable or even deceptive indicator of safety performance.

Like planning, monitoring health and safety performance against pre-determined plans and standards should be a line management responsibility. Monitoring also reinforces management's commitment to health and safety objectives in general and helps in developing a positive health and safety culture by rewarding positive work done to control risk. Two types of system are required:

- **active** systems which monitor the design, development, installation and operation of management arrangements, RCSs and workplace precautions;
- **reactive** systems which monitor accidents, ill health, incidents and other evidence of deficient health and safety performance.

Organisations need to have procedures to allow them to collect the information to adequately investigate the causes of substandard performance.

Active monitoring systems

Active monitoring gives an organisation feedback on its performance **before** an accident, incident or ill health. It includes monitoring the achievement of specific plans and objectives, the operation of the health and safety management system, and compliance with performance standards. This provides a firm basis for decisions about improvements in risk control and the health and safety management system. There are additional benefits, however. Active monitoring measures success and reinforces positive achievement by rewarding good work, rather than penalising failure after the event. Such reinforcement can increase motivation to achieve continued improvement.

Organisations need to decide how to allocate responsibilities for monitoring at different levels in the management chain and what level of detail is appropriate. The decisions will reflect the organisation's structure. Managers should be given the responsibility for monitoring the achievement of objectives and compliance with standards for which they and their subordinates are responsible. Managers and supervisors responsible for direct implementation of standards should monitor compliance in detail. Above this immediate level of control, monitoring needs to be more selective, but provide assurance that adequate first-line monitoring is taking place. This should reflect not only the quantity but the quality of subordinates' monitoring activity.

Multi-site organisations need to satisfy themselves that different 'satellites' are meeting corporate plans and objectives as well as controlling risks. There need to be performance standards for managers to indicate how they will monitor.

The various forms and levels of active monitoring include:

- routine procedures to monitor specific objectives, eg quarterly or monthly reports or returns;
- periodic examination of documents to check that systems relating to the promotion of the health and safety culture are complied with. One example might be the way in which suitable objectives have been established for each manager; regular review of performance; assessment and recording of training needs; and delivery of suitable training;
- the systematic inspection of premises, plant and equipment by supervisors, maintenance staff, management, safety representatives or other employees to ensure the continued effective operation of workplace precautions (see Inset 13);
- environmental monitoring and health surveillance to check on the effectiveness of health control measures and to detect early signs of harm to health;
- systematic direct observation of work and behaviour by first-line supervisors to assess compliance with RCSs and associated procedures and rules, particularly those directly concerned with risk control;
- the operation of audit systems (see Chapter 6);
- consideration of regular reports on health and safety performance by the board of directors.

The key to effective active monitoring is the quality of the plans, performance standards and specifications which have been established and which were described in Chapter 4. These provide the yardstick against which performance can be measured.

Inset 13 **Inspection**

A system for inspecting workplace precautions is important in any active monitoring programme. It can form part of the arrangements for the preventive maintenance of plant and equipment which may also be covered by legal requirements. Equipment in this category includes pressure vessels, lifts, cranes, chains, ropes, lifting tackle, power presses, scaffolds, trench supports and local exhaust ventilation. But inspections should include other workplace precautions, such as those covering the use of premises, other places of work and systems of work.

A suitable programme will take all risks into account but should be properly targeted. For example, low risks might be dealt with by general inspections every month or two covering a wide range of workplace precautions such as the condition of premises, floors, passages, stairs, lighting, welfare facilities and first aid. Higher risks need more frequent and detailed inspections, perhaps weekly or even, in extreme cases, daily or before use. An example of a pre-use check would be the operation of mobile plant.

The inspection programme should satisfy any specific legal requirements and reflect risk priorities. Suitable schedules and performance standards for the frequency and content of inspection can help. The schedules can be supplemented with inspection forms or checklists, both to ensure consistency in approach and to provide records for follow-up action.

Inspections should be done by people who are competent to identify the relevant hazards and risks and who can assess the conditions found. When shortcomings are discovered, the decision processes and actions shown in Diagram 11 should be followed.

A properly thought-out approach to inspection will include:

- well-designed inspection forms to help plan and initiate remedial action by requiring those doing the inspection to rank any deficiencies in order of importance;
- summary lists of remedial action with names and deadlines to track progress on implementing improvements;
- periodic analysis of inspection forms to identify common features or trends which might reveal underlying weaknesses in the system;
- information to aid judgements about any changes required in the frequency or nature of the inspection programme.

Active monitoring should be proportional to the hazard profile (see Inset 12). Activity should concentrate on areas where it is likely to produce the greatest benefit and lead to the greatest control of risk. Key risk control systems and related workplace precautions should therefore be monitored in more detail or more often (or both) than low-risk systems or management arrangements.

Regular monitoring may also be usefully supplemented by:

- random observation including senior managers on 'health and safety tours' (see under 'Communication' in Chapter 3);
- periodic surveys of employees' opinions on key aspects of health and safety. HSE has published a tool to help organisations assess such aspects of their health and safety climate;[29]
- inspections by safety representatives or other employee representatives.

Reactive monitoring systems

Reactive systems, by definition, are triggered after an event and include identifying and reporting:

- injuries and cases of ill health (including monitoring of sickness absence records);
- other losses, such as damage to property;
- incidents, including those with the **potential** to cause injury, ill health or loss;
- hazards;
- weakness or omissions in performance standards.

Each of the above provides opportunities for an organisation to check performance, learn from mistakes, and improve the health and safety management system and risk control. In certain cases, it must send a report of the circumstances and causes to the appropriate enforcing authority. Statutorily appointed safety representatives are entitled to investigate.

Events also contribute to the 'corporate memory'. Information gathered from investigations is a useful way to reinforce key health and safety messages. Common features or trends can be discussed with the workforce, particularly safety representatives. Employees can identify jobs or activities which cause the greatest number of injuries where remedial action may be most beneficial. Investigations may also provide valuable information in the event of an insurance claim or legal action.

Collecting information on serious injuries and ill health should not present major problems for most organisations, but learning about minor injuries, other losses, incidents and hazards can prove more challenging. As shown in Inset 1, there is value in collecting information on all actual and potential losses to learn how to prevent more serious events. Accurate reporting can be promoted by:

- training which clarifies the underlying objectives and reasons for identifying such events;
- a culture which emphasises an observant and responsible approach and the importance of having systems of control in place before harm occurs;
- open, honest communication in a just environment, rather than a tendency merely to allocate 'blame';
- cross-referencing and checking first-aid treatments, health records, maintenance or fire reports and insurance claims to identify any otherwise unreported events.

Investigation and response systems for active and reactive monitoring

A common set of steps can be identified for responding to both active and reactive monitoring. These are summarised in Diagram 11.

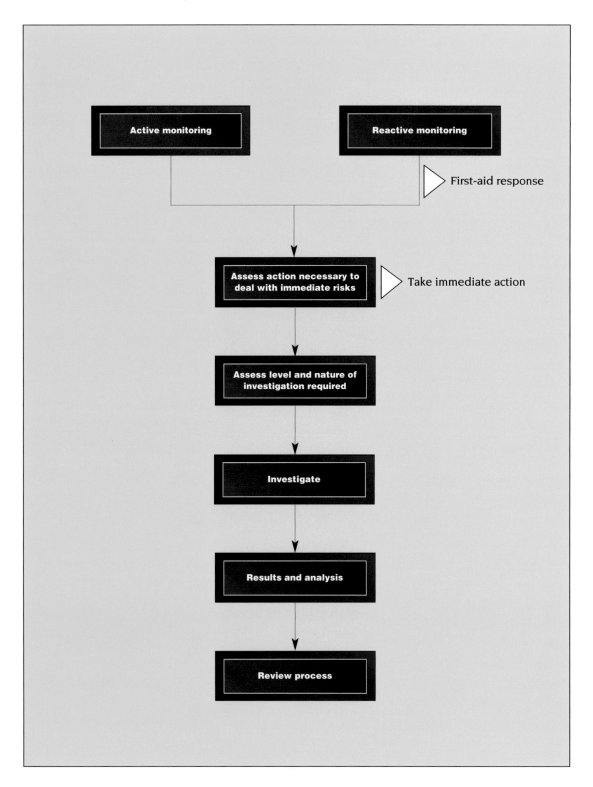

Diagram 11 *Response systems*

Actions necessary to deal with immediate risks

Urgent action may need to be taken if immediate risks become apparent during active monitoring.

Regulation 8 of the MHSW Regulations[18] requires every employer to have appropriate procedures to deal with events involving serious and imminent danger to people at work. If an accident or incident occurs, immediate action may be necessary before any investigation begins, to:

■ help, treat and if necessary rescue the injured;
■ make the situation safe and prevent further injury or damage.

In some cases, for example a major incident, established emergency procedures or disaster management plans may be implemented. (In some industries, eg mining and offshore, specific legislation says that in the case of certain accidents and dangerous occurrences the site must be left undisturbed for a specified time unless disturbance is necessary to make it safe or to rescue people.)

Level and nature of investigation

Not all events need to be investigated to the same extent or depth. Organisations need to assess each event (for instance, using a simple risk-based approach) to identify where the most benefit can be obtained. The greatest effort should concentrate on significant events where there has been serious injury, ill health or loss as well as those which **had the potential** to cause widespread or serious injury or loss. Investigations should:

■ identify reasons for substandard performance;
■ identify underlying failures in health and safety management systems;
■ learn from events;
■ prevent recurrences;
■ satisfy legal and reporting requirements.

The form of investigation

Investigations should be led by someone with the status and knowledge to make authoritative recommendations. Usually, this will be a line manager. A health and safety adviser, a medical or nursing adviser, technical staff or equipment suppliers may need to provide assistance and senior managers may need to be involved if events have serious or potentially serious consequences. Adequate training in the relevant techniques needs to be provided. Safety representatives may also make a valuable contribution.

A good investigation is prompt and thorough. It recommends and assigns remedial actions. If it is not done as soon as practicable after the event, conditions and people's memories can fade. There are four ingredients:

■ **collect evidence** about what has happened;
■ **assemble, and consider** the evidence;
■ **compare** the findings with the appropriate legal, industry and company standards and draw conclusions;
■ **implement** the findings and track progress.

Collecting evidence

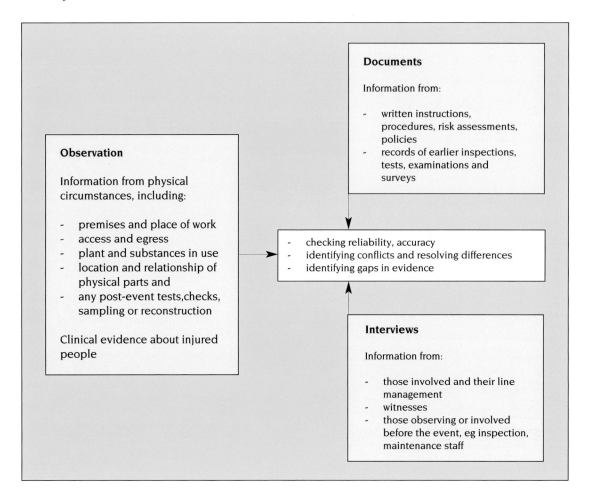

Diagram 12 *Sources of evidence*

Diagram 12 shows the sources of information and methods which investigators can use and emphasises three useful points:

■ **direct observation** is important to avoid losing important evidence about the scene, configuration, relationships between parts etc;

■ **documents** help establish what should have happened as well as providing evidence of prior risk assessment, inspections, tests etc;

■ **interviews** provide both direct testimony as well as an opportunity to check back on any issues arising from examination of the physical and documentary evidence.

Although these are distinct and important elements of a thorough investigation, they complement each other. They provide an opportunity to 'read across' from one part of the process to another to check reliability and accuracy as well as to resolve differences and gaps in evidence. Elsewhere in this guidance, we have emphasised that accidents and incidents seldom arise from a single cause: there are usually underlying failures in the management system itself which have helped create the circumstances leading to the event.

Assembling and considering the evidence

Good investigations identify both immediate and underlying causes, including human factors. Immediate causes include the job being done and the people involved. Underlying causes are the management and organisational factors which explain why the event occurred. Examples of both are shown in Diagram 13. The underlying causes shown correspond to the management model outlined in this guidance. Appendix 5 contains a sequence which you can follow to identify underlying causes more systematically.

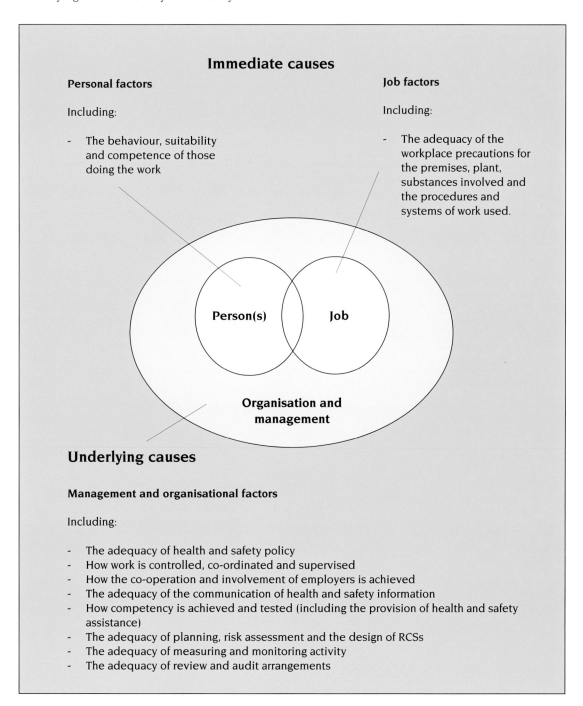

Immediate causes

Personal factors

Including:

- The behaviour, suitability and competence of those doing the work

Job factors

Including:

- The adequacy of the workplace precautions for the premises, plant, substances involved and the procedures and systems of work used.

Person(s)   **Job**

Organisation and management

Underlying causes

Management and organisational factors

Including:

- The adequacy of health and safety policy
- How work is controlled, co-ordinated and supervised
- How the co-operation and involvement of employers is achieved
- The adequacy of the communication of health and safety information
- How competency is achieved and tested (including the provision of health and safety assistance)
- The adequacy of planning, risk assessment and the design of RCSs
- The adequacy of measuring and monitoring activity
- The adequacy of review and audit arrangements

Diagram 13 A framework for analysing accident and incident causation

Comparing conditions with relevant specifications and standards

The next stage of investigation is to compare the conditions and sequence of events with relevant standards which represent legal minimum requirements of good practice. This helps to minimise the subjective nature of investigations and to generate recommendations which have the maximum impact and relevance. The objectives are to decide:

■　if suitable specifications or standards have been set to control all the factors influencing the event. These need to consider all the causes identified in the framework within Diagram 13, paying particular attention to legal standards and the preventive and protective measures identified by risk assessment;

■　if specifications or standards existed, were they appropriate and sufficient?

■　if the specifications or standards were good enough, were they applied and implemented in practice?

■　why any failures occurred.

This approach leads to conclusions which identify:

■　where specifications or standards and controls for risks and organisational elements are absent;

■　where specifications or standards are inadequate; and

■　where specifications or standards are adequate but not properly implemented.

Implementing findings and tracking progress

The final step is to ensure that recommendations are given priorities and turned into objectives for people to implement. This step forms the basis for the review process. To set priorities, organisations may need to apply a simplified process for prioritising, based on risk assessment as described in Chapter 4.

Outputs and analysis

Standard report forms can usefully guide people through the investigation processes outlined above and help the managers responsible for authorising necessary follow-up actions to set priorities. Inset 14 gives further details. More generally, the recording system should:

■　collect information accurately and present it in a consistent form;

■　enable analysis to identify common causes, features and trends which may not be apparent from the investigation of an individual event;

■　record information which might foreseeably be needed in the future or which may also be useful for management purposes, to record time taken to carry out the investigation and the related costs;

■　alert others to the learning points from a single or a series of events.

A number of proprietary computerised accident recording and analysis programmes are available which can help analyse collected data to look for common features and underlying organisational causes. Organisations need to carry out periodic reviews of report forms to check that any remedial actions identified have been adequate, appropriate and implemented. This is dealt with in Chapter 6.

Inset 14 **Key data to be covered in accident, ill health and incident reports**

The event

■ Details of any injured person, including age, sex, experience, training etc.

■ A description of the circumstances, including the place, time of day and conditions.

■ Details of the event, including:
▨ any actions which led directly to the event;
▨ the direct causes of any injuries, ill health or other loss;
▨ the immediate causes of the event;
▨ the underlying causes - for example, failures in workplace precautions, risk control systems or management arrangements (see Appendix 5).

■ Details of the outcomes, including in particular:
▨ the nature of the outcome - for example, injuries, or ill health to employees or members of the public; damage to property; process disruptions; emissions to the environment; creation of hazards;
▨ the severity of the harm caused, including injuries, ill health and losses;
▨ the immediate management response to the situation and its adequacy:
  - Was it dealt with promptly?
  - Were continuing risks dealt with promptly and adequately?
  - Was the first-aid response adequate?
  - Were emergency procedures followed?
▨ Whether the event was preventable and if so how.

The potential consequences

■ What was the worst that could have happened?
■ What prevented the worst from happening?
■ How often could such an event occur (the **'recurrence potential'**)?
■ What was the worst injury or damage which could have resulted (the **'severity potential'**)?
■ How many people could the event have affected (the **'population potential'**)?

continued overleaf

65

Inset 14 (*continued*)

Recommendations

Prioritised actions with responsibilities and targets for completion.

CHAPTER SIX

Auditing and reviewing performance

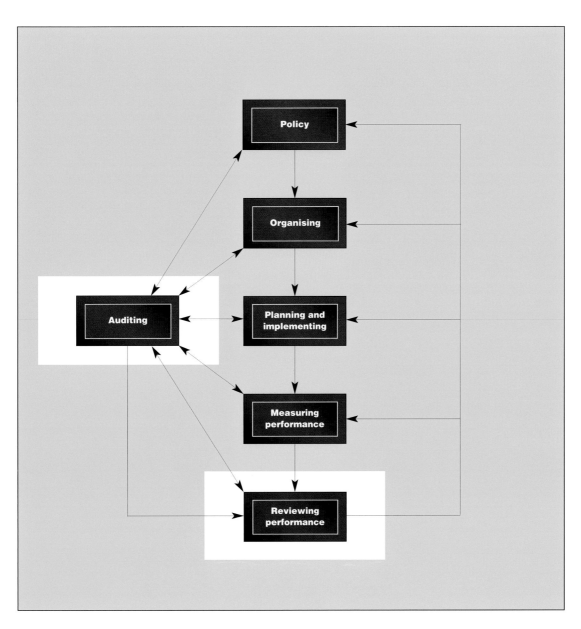

KEY MESSAGES

Organisations can maintain and improve their ability to manage risks by learning from experience through the use of audits and performance reviews. This chapter:

defines the nature and purpose of a health and safety audit;

examines how health and safety performance can be reviewed.

Auditing and performance review are the final steps in the health and safety management control cycle. They constitute the 'feedback loop' which enables an organisation to reinforce, maintain and develop its ability to reduce risks to the fullest extent and to ensure the continued effectiveness of the health and safety management system.

Auditing performance

Organisations are often subject to audit, eg for finance, environment and quality. This business discipline can be applied to health and safety. There are legal definitions of auditing in regulations dealing with safety case requirements for the offshore,[22] gas[30] and railway industries.[25] Some organisations use 'audit' to mean inspections or other monitoring activities, but here we use the following definition:

> *The structured process of collecting independent information on the efficiency, effectiveness and reliability of the total health and safety management system and drawing up plans for corrective action.*

All control systems tend to deteriorate over time or to become obsolete as a result of change. Auditing supports monitoring by providing managers with information on how effectively plans and the components of the health and safety management system are being implemented. It should also provide a check on the adequacy and effectiveness of the management arrangements and RCSs.

Auditing is an essential element of a health and safety management system, and is no substitute for the other essential parts of the system. Organisations cannot manage finances by an annual financial audit; they need systems to pay bills and manage cash flow throughout the year. Similarly, organisations need systems to manage health and safety on a day-to-day basis. This cannot be achieved by a periodic audit.

In Chapter 4 the three components of a health and safety management system were described (see Diagram 9). Over time, auditing should be used to verify the adequacy of each of these components. For multi-site organisations, auditing should include the management arrangements linking the centre with the business units and sites.

The aims of auditing should be to establish that:

■ appropriate management arrangements are in place;
■ adequate risk control systems exist, are implemented, and consistent with the hazard profile of the organisation;
■ appropriate workplace precautions are in place.

Various methods can achieve this and some components of the system do not need to be audited as often as others. For instance an audit of the management arrangements and the overall capability of an organisation to manage health and safety need not be done as often as an audit to verify the implementation of RCSs. It is also more beneficial to audit more frequently critical RCSs which control the main hazards of the business. 'Technical' audits may be necessary to verify the continued effectiveness of complex workplace precautions, eg process plant integrity and control systems.

A comprehensive picture of how effectively the health and safety management system is controlling risks will emerge from a well-structured auditing programme indicating when and how each component part will be audited. A team approach, involving managers, safety representatives and employees is an effective way to widen involvement and co-operation in devising and implementing the programme.

The auditing process involves:

■ collecting information about the health and safety management system; and
■ making judgements about its adequacy and performance.

Collecting information

Collecting information about health and safety management requires decisions on the level and detail of an audit. All audits involve sampling and a key question is always: 'How much sampling needs to be done to make a reliable assessment?' The nature and complexity of an audit will therefore vary according to its objectives and scope; the size, sophistication and complexity of the organisation; and the maturity of the existing health and safety management system.

Auditors have three information sources on which to draw:

■ **Interviewing individuals**, to gain information about the operation of the health and safety management system and the perceptions, knowledge, understanding, management practices, skill and competence of managers and employees at various levels in the organisation.

- **Examining documents**, assessing records, RCSs, performance standards, procedures and instructions for completeness, accuracy and reliability together with the implications for competence and understanding - in practice these may need to be reviewed in preparing the audit to identify issues to follow up and people to interview.

- **Visual observation** of physical conditions and work activities to examine compliance with legal requirements and verify the implementation and effectiveness of workplace precautions and RCSs.

These information sources are usually used in the following sequence:

Preparation

- Discuss and agree the objectives and scope of the audit with relevant managers and employee representatives.
- Collect and review documentation.
- Prepare and agree audit plan.

On-site

- Interview people.
- Review and assess additional documents.
- Observe physical conditions and work activities.

Conclusion

- Assemble and evaluate evidence.
- Write audit report.

Making judgements

The adequacy of a health and safety management system is judged by making a comparison between what is found against a relevant 'standard' or benchmark. If there are no clear standards, the assessment process will be unreliable. Legal standards, HSE guidance and applicable industry standards should be used to inform audit judgements. Benchmarks for management arrangements and design of RCSs are set out in this book.

It is important that auditing is not perceived as a fault-finding activity but as a valuable contribution to the health and safety management system and learning. Auditing should recognise positive achievements as well as areas for improvement.

In some audits, scoring systems are used to complement judgements and recommendations. This can help with comparing audit scores over time or between sites, but there is no evidence to suggest that quantifying the results yields a better response than an approach providing only qualitative evidence. Scoring systems can, however, introduce other difficulties, eg managers aiming their attention at high-scoring questions irrespective of their relevance to developing the health and safety management system.

Audit controls

Like any process, there need to be controls to ensure that an audit is applied rigorously and consistently. An unreliable system may lead managers to lose confidence in its relevance and validity. Typical controls:

- ensure that the audit is perceived as a positive management tool and is taken seriously by all levels of management;
- ensure that the system is applied in accordance with its intended use. Using the system for other than its designed purpose may reduce the return on the investment in auditing. Stricter controls may be necessary where number scoring systems are used. Inconsistent application may invalidate the potential for comparison;
- secure the competence of auditors. All systems, to varying degrees, rely on the competence of auditors. Specific standards of training and assessment are valuable to ensure consistency of method and interpretation;
- secure the effective implementation of results and recommendations.

To maximise the benefits, audits should be conducted by competent people independent of the area or activities being audited. This can be achieved by using staff from different sections, departments or sites to audit their colleagues or by using external consultants. Organisations can use either their own self-developed auditing system, those marketed as proprietary systems or a combination of both. It is unlikely that any one proprietary system will suit an organisation perfectly. Usually a scheme has to be tailored to individual requirements and the choice is influenced by the costs and potential benefits. Common problems include:

- the system is too broad-brush and may require considerable work to fit the needs and hazard profile of the particular user;
- the system may be too bureaucratic for the style and culture of the organisation;
- scoring systems may mask a deterioration in performance if the underlying detail is not examined;
- organisations may create a management system which achieves high scores rather than one which suits the needs and hazard profile of the business.

HSE encourages organisations to assess their health and safety management systems using in-house or proprietary schemes but without endorsing any particular one. Some of the key characteristics of effective audit systems are summarised in Inset 15.

Inset 15 **Effective health and safety audit systems**

Effective auditing systems display the following characteristics:

■ They are carried out by a competent individual or team who have received specific training to do the work (this may involve a team of managers, specialists, other employees or their representatives, or external consultants).

■ The auditor(s) is independent of the area or section being audited.

Audits are designed to assess the following key elements of health and safety management:

Policy

■ Its intent, scope and adequacy.

Organisation

■ The acceptance of health and safety responsibilities by line managers and the adequacy of arrangements to secure control.

■ The adequacy of arrangements to consult and involve all employees in health and safety.

■ The adequacy of arrangements to communicate policy and relevant information.

■ The adequacy of arrangements to secure the competence of all employees and the provision of health and safety assistance.

Planning and implementation

■ The overall control and direction of the health and safety effort.

■ The adequacy of the management arrangements, RCSs and workplace precautions.

■ The adequacy of resources and their proportionate allocation to reflect the hazard profile of the business.

■ The extent of compliance with management arrangements, RCSs, performance standards and the effectiveness of workplace precautions in achieving control of risk.

■ Long-term improvement in the accident and incident performance.

Measuring systems

■ Their adequacy, relevance and design.

Review systems

■ The ability of the organisation to learn from experience, improve performance, develop the health and safety management system, and respond to change.

The Offshore Installations (Safety Case) Regulations 1992,[22] the Railways (Safety Case) Regulations 1994,[25] and the Gas Safety (Management) Regulations 1996,[30] require the arrangements for audit to be set out in the safety case. Elsewhere, performance standards should be devised for planning and implementing the audit programme and these standards should themselves be monitored. Some organisations allocate responsibility for health and safety auditing to their internal auditing sections in an attempt to integrate health and safety management more fully into their existing structures.

Reviewing performance

Reviewing is the process of making judgements about the adequacy of performance and taking decisions about the nature and timing of the actions necessary to remedy deficiencies. Organisations need to have feedback to see if the health and safety management system is working effectively as designed. The main sources of information come from measuring activities and from audits of the RCSs and workplace precautions. Other internal and external influences include delayering, new legislation or changes in current good practice. Any of these can result in redesign or amendment of any parts of the health and safety management system or a change in overall direction or objectives. Suitable performance standards should be established to identify the responsibilities, timing and systems involved.

Feeding information on success and failure back into the system is an essential element in motivating employees to maintain and improve performance. Successful organisations emphasise positive reinforcement and concentrate on encouraging progress on those indicators which demonstrate improvements in risk control.

The aims of the review process reflect the objectives of the planning process. Reviews will need to examine:

■ the operation and maintenance of the system as designed; and
■ the design, development and installation of the health and safety management system in changing circumstances.

Reviewing should be a continuous process undertaken at different levels within the organisation. It includes responses:

■ by first-line supervisors or other managers to remedy failures to implement workplace precautions which they observe in the course of routine activities;
■ to remedy sub-standard performance identified by active and reactive monitoring;
■ to the assessment of plans at individual, departmental, site, group or organisational level;
■ to the results of audits.

Review plans may include:

■ monthly reviews of individuals, supervisors or sections;

- three-monthly reviews of departments;
- annual reviews of sites or of the organisation as a whole.

Organisations should decide on the frequency of the reviews at each level and devise reviewing activities to suit the measuring and auditing activities. In all reviewing activity the result should be specific remedial actions which:

- establish who is responsible for implementation; and
- set deadlines for completion.

These actions form the basis of effective follow-up, which should be closely monitored.

The speed and nature of response to any situation should be determined by the degree of risk involved and the availability of resources. The application of risk assessment principles outlined in Chapter 4 can contribute to decision-making by identifying relative priorities. Reviewing demands the exercise of good judgement, and people responsible for reviewing may need specific training to achieve competence in this type of task.

Key performance indicators for reviewing overall performance can include:

- assessment of the degree of compliance with health and safety system requirements;
- identification of areas where the health and safety system is absent or inadequate (those areas where further action is necessary to develop the total health and safety management system);
- assessment of the achievement of specific objectives and plans; and
- accident, ill health and incident data accompanied by analysis of both the immediate and underlying causes, trends and common features.

These indicators are consistent with the development of a positive health and safety culture. They emphasise achievement and success rather than merely measuring failure by looking only at accident data.

Organisations may also 'benchmark' their performance against other organisations by comparing:

- accident rates with those organisations in the same industry which use similar business processes and experience similar risks (see Appendix 6 for more information on calculating and using accident incidence and frequency rates); and
- management practices and techniques with other organisations in any industry to provide a different perspective and new insights on health and safety management systems.

As part of a demonstration of corporate responsibility, more organisations are mentioning health and safety performance in their published annual reports.

APPENDICES

1 - 6

Appendix 1 *Terminology*

In this guidance:

Policy is used in relation to health and safety and other functional management areas (eg manufacturing and human resources) to convey:

■ the general intentions, approach and objectives of an organisation; and
■ the criteria and principles on which its actions and responses are based.

The term 'written policy statements' means documents that record the policy of the organisation.

Organisation means the responsibilities and relationships between individuals which form the social environment in which work takes place.

Organising means the process of designing and establishing these responsibilities and relationships. The expression 'statements of organisation' is used to describe documents that record those responsibilities and relationships.

Organisation also refers to any undertaking subject to the HSW Act, including:

■ companies and firms in the extractive, manufacturing, construction, agricultural, transport and service industries;
■ commercial and financial institutions, such as banks, building societies and insurance companies;
■ public utilities and institutions, such as the health service, research laboratories, colleges, universities and local authorities;
■ non-profit-making institutions, such as charities.

Accident includes any undesired circumstances which give rise to ill health or injury; damage to property, plant, products or the environment; production losses or increased liabilities.

Incident includes all undesired circumstances and 'near misses' which could cause accidents.

Hazard means the potential to cause:

■ harm including ill health and injury;
■ damage to property, plant, products or the environment;
■ production losses or increased liabilities.

Ill health includes acute and chronic ill health caused by physical, chemical or biological agents as well as adverse effects on mental health.

Risk means the likelihood that a specified undesired event will occur due to the realisation of a hazard by, or during, work activities or by the products and services created by work activities.

RCSs means risk control system(s).

Planning means the process by which the objectives and methods of implementing the health and safety policy are decided. It is concerned with allocating resources (eg money, time or effort) to achieve objectives and decide priorities. It ranges from general topics dealing with the direction of the whole organisation to detailed issues concerned with standard-setting and the control of specific risks.

Measuring means the collection of information about the implementation and effectiveness of plans and standards. This involves various checking or 'monitoring' activities.

Auditing is the structured process of collecting independent information on the efficiency, effectiveness and reliability of the total health and safety management system and drawing up plans for corrective action.

Reviewing means activities involving judgements about performance, and decisions about improving performance. Reviewing is based on information from 'measuring' and 'auditing' activities.

Appendix 2 *Organising for health and safety*

Key tasks for policy makers, planners and implementers of policy

Policy makers

The key **tasks** of policy makers include:

- devising health and safety policy;
- establishing strategies to implement policy and integrating these into general business activity;
- specifying a structure for planning, measuring, reviewing and auditing health and safety policy;
- specifying a structure for implementing policy and supporting plans;
- agreeing plans for improvement and reviewing progress to develop both the health and safety management system and the policy;
- pursuing health and safety objectives with evident sincerity.

The major **outputs** include:

- written statements of general health and safety policy and strategic objectives;
- written statements of the organisation for planning, measuring, reviewing and auditing;
- written statements of the organisation for implementation;
- general plans containing specific objectives for each year.

Planners

The key **tasks** of planners include:

- producing detailed plans to achieve corporate health and safety objectives;
- establishing management arrangements, risk control systems and workplace precautions together with associated performance standards;
- co-ordinating the specialist advice needed to ensure effective planning and implementation of policy, for example the input of health and safety specialists, engineers, architects and doctors;
- ensuring the participation and involvement of employees and their representatives;
- keeping up to date with changes in health and safety legislation, standards and good practice and with management practices relevant to the organisation.

The key **outputs** include:

- health and safety strategy statements and plans to support the policy;
- health and safety operational plans which identify specific health and safety objectives to be achieved within fixed time periods;

- specifications for management arrangements, RCS(s), workplace precautions and performance standards;
- up-to-date documentation.

Implementers

The key tasks for **implementers** are:

- implementation of operational plans, management arrangements, RCSs, workplace precautions and performance standards;
- provision of necessary physical and human resources and information;
- provision of timely feedback on performance including successes and failures and any deficiencies in plans, arrangements, systems or precautions;
- ensuring communication and participation at all levels in health and safety activities.

The key **outputs** are:

- safe and healthy production and delivery of products and services;
- products and services which in themselves do not create risks to others.

Appendix 3 *Reorganisation*

Reorganisation (also known by the terms delayering, downsizing and re-engineering, among others) has continued to occur in all sectors of activity since this guidance was first issued. This affects the ways organisations exercise their control functions. HSE-sponsored research[12] during 1996 drew on published literature and the experiences of ten very different organisations to provide practical guidance - illustrated with case-study examples - on how to carry out reorganisation without jeopardising health and safety standards. The main findings were:

- many large organisations were shifting from a hierarchical command structure to flatter and more customer-oriented structures;
- organisations first streamlined in response to cost pressures and then sought more radical solutions;
- delayering was often accompanied by outsourcing, changes in systems of work, reward and promotion systems, attitudes, management style, accountability, empowerment, multi-skilling and team working;
- the success rate of business re-engineering was mixed, with reports of both significant improvement in profits and lacklustre results;
- the mixed results of re-engineering projects were due to poorly carried-out changes, such as setting simplistic goals and failing to train people.

The research concluded that the principles in this guidance can be used as a model for reorganisation and for achieving satisfactory health and safety standards subsequently. If it also introduces a more participative style of management, these principles may become even more relevant.

The relationship between management approach, competence and operational risk

The research confirmed that a three-way balance needs to be struck between:

- the degree of supervision, management systems, engineered safety systems, rules and procedures;
- competence; and
- inherent operational risk.

Some of the conclusions relevant to this guidance are listed below.

Assuring competence

Where responsibility for health and safety is clearly given to line managers, a major programme of management training is likely to be needed (see Inset 8). The role of any retained health and safety adviser(s) changes and they have an influential role in establishing central policies, rules and guidance, providing training and technical support, and carrying out auditing (see Inset 9).

A frequent aim of reorganisation is to enhance individuals' contributions to the business by giving them wider and more flexible roles. Team working is commonly introduced, with team members empowered to agree task-specific roles among themselves. The supervisor's role can change from one of deciding how to complete a job and directing others in their work, to one based on team leadership without authority or technical control. This requires different skills (see Inset 6).

The successful introduction of multi-skilling and team work depends on ensuring that group members between them possess all the skills and experience to carry out the work. One organisation achieved this by exempting staff with core skills from redundancy, and using retraining needs analysis to ensure there were no skills gaps. This had four stages:

- Identify changes in tasks, jobs and/or allocation of duties.
- Identify changes in core skills, experience and knowledge requirements of the organisation.
- Assess competence of personnel.
- Define and execute selection, re-training, job definition and development programme.

This analysis was applied to all grades, and included general technical, operational, and management skills as well as specific health and safety skills.

Outsourcing

Typically, the importance of management of health and safety by contractors and the nature of the management task for the host organisation change following reorganisation. The range of outsourced tasks, and therefore the number of contractors involved, may increase substantially. By contrast, the resources retained in-house to manage outsourcing may be reduced as a part of the reorganisation. Some typical examples of outsourced activities include:

- major maintenance, design, engineering and commissioning projects;
- transport of hazardous materials;
- plant operation;
- routine maintenance;
- cleaning.

The research identified five issues to address under this heading:

- Does the rigour of contractor management match the risk from the outsourced activities?
- Has the nature of outsourced work changed?
- What balance can be struck between contractor supervision and contractor self-management?
- How familiar is the contractor with the client's hazards and procedures?
- Are new forms of contractor assessment required (such as auditing)?

Strategies may be needed to develop contractor competence and to upgrade arrangements for verifying that contractors manage their affairs properly. Actions by the researched organisations included:

- secondment or transfer of own staff to contractors;
- formation of a long-term relationship with contractors;
- incorporating contractors into the host's health and safety management system;
- requiring long-term contractors to produce 'safety cases';
- shared basic training of contractors across local industry;
- measuring contractor health and safety performance;
- operating approved contractor lists.

Performance measurement

Setting relevant standards against which performance can genuinely be measured becomes even more important after activities are outsourced, and contractual arrangements have been introduced.

Conclusion

The research concluded that the impact of reorganisation depends on how well the organisation assesses the implications and plans the changes. Health and safety performance was reported to improve where well-planned and well-resourced schemes were introduced. In some cases it was considered that the improvements could not have been achieved under the traditional organisational structure and style of management. Reorganisation can, however, be a major source of stress. It has also been identified as a factor contributing to a number of major accidents involving multiple fatalities.

Appendix 4 *Implementation of health and safety management systems*

There is no single way to develop and implement a system, but there are some general issues upon which management can usefully focus. They reinforce many of the key messages elsewhere in this guidance and show that implementing a health and safety management system is no different to implementing any other management system.

Obstacles

One of the major obstacles to implementation is that some managers have difficulty in understanding what a health and safety management system is. A commonly held view is that health and safety management is simply a diverse collection of activities required by law. The challenge to organisations is to recognise the complete range of activities required to create the management framework as illustrated in Diagram 1.

There is a parallel view that the activities are complex or require specialist knowledge and are therefore best left to the health and safety specialist. HSE research contradicts this and confirms that successful health and safety achievement requires active line management commitment.

The impetus for change

Organisations may have several reasons for improving their performance and developing the health and safety management system. Common ones are:

- a new chief executive or senior manager;
- change of ownership;
- pressure from suppliers, customers or shareholders;
- a dramatic incident;
- pressure from the regulator.

Whatever the trigger, the key issues are the same.

The implementation process

The organisation has to have a clear idea of what the end product of the implementation process will be and how to achieve it. The focus or emphasis can change as the system develops but common themes or underlying principles need to remain consistent. For example, if employee involvement is an underlying principle, it needs to be applied for each and every activity in the implementation process.

Organising: control

Key appointments

A senior manager needs to be appointed and to accept responsibility for the implementation process. This appointment can send powerful signals about the importance of health and safety and drive the process forward. A second key appointment is to select someone responsible for the design and architecture of the management system itself. It may be the same senior manager or someone different, but both individuals need to be able to demonstrate:

■ sufficient vision to be able to use the principles of health and safety management to create the system architecture and guidelines to help others carry out the implementation;

■ the necessary leadership, drive and self-belief to see the implementation through to completion.

Formation of a steering committee

Many organisations set up a steering committee which includes other senior line managers to organise the process. This is a key feature in transferring 'ownership' of safety from its traditional location with the safety adviser to the direct line function. Typically, the role of the steering group is to draw up the implementation plan, allocate responsibilities and monitor progress.

An initial review of the health and safety management system is sometimes undertaken. This answers the question 'Where are we now?' The steering committee evaluates any recommendations emerging from this review and incorporates the findings in the implementation plan. Sub-committees may be set up to support the work.

Selection and appointment of co-ordinators

On larger sites or in multi-site organisations, it may be appropriate to appoint local co-ordinators who can act as 'champions' of the health and safety management system and further help in transferring ownership.

Organising: co-operation

Involvement of the workforce

All the organisations that participated in the HSE study believed that involving the workforce was vital to success. As a way to achieve it, they used specific initiatives, problem solving and participation on the various committees/working groups associated with implementation. In many cases, step improvements only occurred after this happened. However, the workforce will only engage when management have shown their personal and long-term commitment.

Multi-site organisations can develop generic solutions at individual sites as a way to share experience, workload and best practice. This also avoids reinventing solutions.

Organising: competence

Competence issues have been discussed in Chapter 3. Timing of health and safety management training is critical. Organisations have usually found that they would have preferred to have provided it earlier than they did. It is particularly important at the outset that senior management understand the aim and objectives of the health and safety management system, the principles on which it is to operate and how they should support both the process and the subordinates involved.

Organising: communication

Communication of intent and demonstration of commitment

Everyone in the organisation needs to know what the implementation plans are and how they are progressing. Success depends on a visible demonstration by senior management in leading and supporting the process.

Planning

Implementation plan

A key output from the steering committee or the system architect is an implementation plan which serves as the blueprint for action. Key milestones for implementation and success criteria should be determined, set and regularly reviewed by management.

The health and safety management system manual/key procedures

How far the system needs to be documented will depend on any particular legal requirement and the overall style and approach to written communication within the organisation. Organisations may find it helpful to produce a health and safety management manual covering the principles and management arrangements. Preparing such a manual can be an important output from the steering committee.

Recognition of the 'people' issues

Change creates uncertainty and concern. Its effect on people's feelings must be considered as part of the implementation process. One way of recognising and acting on this is to devote more attention to communications, involvement and training. The approach to new ways of working for health and safety can also contribute to a change of culture across the business in the longer term. Health and safety can act as a vehicle for broader organisational change. The effect of introducing the health and safety management system needs to be considered both in terms of the opportunity it presents and potential for conflict with other existing business arrangements.

Measurement

The implementation process itself needs to be measured. Some multi-site organisations have used a weighted implementation plan to help drive the process at subsidiary level. Other key implementation measurement activities are the monitoring of the activities necessary to achieve the objectives of the implementation plan, the quality of the outputs achieved and the timescales involved.

Audit and review

Periodic reviews are necessary to ensure that the process is on track and continuing to meet its objectives. As overall health and safety management competence and 'feel' for the system improves, initial assumptions will alter. Other business changes and initiatives will have materialised and will need to be incorporated in the implementation plan. Reviews need to take account of the information generated from the measurement process and how to initiate any necessary remedial actions.

Auditing is a common way to assess implementation progress particularly when an initial audit can act as a benchmark. It can be useful to examine the quality of the system being created as well as the degree to which the gaps are being closed. Following audit and review, the cycle of organising, planning, measurement and review is likely to recur as part of a wider process of continuous improvement.

Timescales

A key message which emerged from HSE contact with organisations is that implementing an effective health and safety management system takes time. Two to five years is typical.

Appendix 5 *Analysing the causes of accidents and incidents*

The following sequence is one approach which may be used as a guide to analysing the immediate and underlying causes of events. It may be used as a basis for designing an approach which suits the individual needs of the organisation.

The adequacy of workplace precautions should be considered first to identify immediate causes. Consider in turn each of the first four boxes. Follow the directions to other boxes to complete the analysis of all immediate and underlying causes.

All immediate and underlying causes are in one sense a failing to devise and implement an adequate health and safety policy. Policy is an all-embracing aspect and without further specification is not useful as a basis for remedial action. For this reason the policy element of the management arrangements is not identified as a separate category within this framework.

Immediate causes

---

1   Premises

Consider the premises and place of work first and ask 'Was there anything about the place, the access or egress which contributed to the event?' eg holes in floors causing tripping, inadequate ventilation, inadequate weather protection. The most likely conclusions may be:

- Premises not a significant factor - go to 2.
- Adequate premises/access/egress provided but not used - consider working procedures - go to 3.
- Adequate place etc once provided but not maintained - consider planning - go to 5.
- Adequate place etc never provided - consider planning - go to 5.

---

2   Plant and substances

Consider the precautions for plant, equipment and substances and ask 'Was there anything about the adequacy of the controls which contributed to the event?' eg inadequate guarding, poor local exhaust ventilation. (Remember plant and substances may be products supplied by your company.)

The most likely conclusions may be:

- Plant and substances not a significant factor - go to 3.
- Adequate controls provided but not used - consider working procedures - go to 3.
- Adequate controls once provided but not maintained - consider planning - go to 5.
- Adequate controls etc never provided - consider planning - go to 5.

---

3   Procedures

Consider the systems, instructions and methods of work and ask if they contributed to the event, eg failure to use good equipment properly. (Consider both normal operation and emergency procedures.)

The most likely conclusions may be:

- Correct system/method in use - go to 4.

- Correct system/method devised but not used. If so, consider:
- clarity and adequacy of instructions - go to 9;
- adequacy of supervision - go to 7;
- behaviour of person - go to 4.

- Correct system/method once devised and used but now lapsed. Consider:
- adequacy of monitoring - go to 11.

- Correct system/method never devised - consider planning - go to 5.

4   People

Consider the behaviour of the people involved and ask: 'Did they do or fail to do anything which contributed to the event?' The most likely conclusion may be:

- Behaviour not a significant factor.

- People unsuitable for the job (eg physical disability, sensitivity to certain chemicals). Consider whether the person was:
- never suitable - look at recruitment/selection/placement - go to 10;
- once suitable - consider the adequacy of health surveillance - go to 6.

- Suitable person but not competent - consider whether the person was:
- never competent - look at training - go to 10;
- once competent but performance not sustained - look at supervision (go to 7) and monitoring (go to 11).

- Suitable competent person but did wrong thing. Possibilities include:
- unintended actions:
    - slip - doing the right thing in the wrong way;
    - lapse - forgetting the right thing.
- intended actions:
    - mistake - choosing the wrong action in error;
    - violation - purposely doing wrong thing - routine/non-routine.

  Consider:
    - training - go to 10.   -   communication - go to 9.
    - controls/supervision - go to 7.   -   planning - go to 5.
    - monitoring - go to 11.   -   co-operation - go to 8.

Underlying causes - Failures in risk control systems - Management arrangements

---

5   Planning

Risk control systems (RCSs) are necessary for the supply, use, maintenance, demolition and disposal of premises and the supply, storage, handling, use, transport and disposal of plant (including all types of equipment), and substances.

Where inadequate premises, plant and substances or procedures have been provided, consider the adequacy of the RCSs for the:

Premises

- Design of structures/buildings.
- Control of structural design changes.
- Selection of buildings/workplaces.
- Purchase of buildings/workplaces.
- Maintenance of buildings/workplaces.
- Security.
- Demolition.

Procedures

- Preparation, circulation, revision.
- Practicality.
- 'Technical adequacy'.

Plant and substances

- Design of plant/equipment.
- Control of design changes.
- Selection of plant/equipment.
- Supply of plant.
- Selection or purchase of substances.
- Supply of substances.
- Construction and installation of plant.
- Transport of plant and substances.
- Maintenance.
- Commissioning.
- Selection of equipment on hire.
- Control of equipment in use by contractors.
- Changes to process/plant/equipment/ substances.
- Emergency arrangements.
- Decommissioning/dismantling.
- Disposal of plant and substances.

Where RCSs are absent or inadequate, consider risk assessment arrangements - go to 6.

Where RCSs are not used, consider:

- Risk assessment - go to 6.
- Communication - go to 9.
- Organisation: control - go to 7.
- People - go to 4.
- Monitoring - go to 11.

Where procedures involve contractors, consider competence - go to 10.

6   Assessing risks

Consider the adequacy of risk assessment arrangements - if methods of hazard identification and risk assessment are:

- Absent - consider organisation: control - go to 7.
- Inadequate - consider competence of those choosing them - go to 10.
- Adequate but not used, consider:
- organisation: control - go to 7;
- monitoring - go to 11.

- Satisfactory but the results are inadequate - consider:
- competency of those using them - go to 10;
- adequacy of technical standards used - go to 9;
- clarity of results - go to 9;
- involvement of employees - go to 8.

7   Organisation: control

Where arrangements/procedures/systems are absent, not used or supervision is inadequate, consider the responsibilities of those devising, operating and maintaining the procedures/systems. Ask:

- Are responsibilities clearly set out?
- Are responsibilities clearly understood?
- Do those with responsibilities have the time and resource to discharge their responsibilities?
- Are people held accountable for discharging health and safety responsibilities?
- Are people rewarded for good performance?
- Are people penalised for poor performance?

If not, consider:

- competence - go to 10;
- the adequacy of senior manager commitment and resources devoted to health and safety.

8   Organisation: co-operation

Consider how those working with risks are involved in risk assessments and devising procedures (including the operation of any health and safety committee). If inadequate consider:

- competence - go to 10.
- the adequacy of senior management commitment to co-operation.

9   Organisation: communication

Consider:

- Is there sufficient, up-to-date information on law and technical standards to make good decisions about how to control risks?
- Are written instructions for internal use clear and in sufficient detail?
- Are the up-to-date versions of instructions available?
- Is there sufficient information supplied to the users of products?
- Is there sufficient visible senior management commitment to health and safety.

10   Organisation: competence

Consider the adequacy of arrangements for:

- recruitment/selection and placement to check that people have the right physical and mental abilities for their jobs including, where necessary, medical examinations, and tests of physical fitness, aptitudes or abilities;
- assessing the health and safety competence of contractors as part of contractor selection;
- identifying health and safety training needs at recruitment, when there are changes in staff, plant, substances, technology, processes or working practices. The need to maintain or enhance competence by refresher training, and the presence of contractors' employees, the self-employed or temporary workers (and assessments of competence);
- competent cover for staff absences, particularly for those people with critical health and safety responsibilities and emergency procedures;
- health checks and health surveillance based on risk assessments (including assessments of fitness for work, following injury or ill health);
- provision of health and safety assistance.

11   **Monitoring**

Consider the adequacy of the checks and inspections made of the workplace precautions and risk control systems before an accident (ie were they frequent enough, and did they look at the right things in sufficient detail to ensure the safe use of premises, plant and substances and the implementation of procedures). If checks were:

- absent - consider organisation: control - go to 7.
- not adequate - review risk assessment arrangements - go to 6.
- not completed - consider organisation: control - go to 7, and review - go to 12.

Consider any previous accident/incident events similar to this one and examine if the investigation or lessons are helpful. If previous events have not been thoroughly investigated, consider:

- the organisation: control - go to 7.
- competence - go to 10.

If the lessons have not been put into effect, consider:

- organisation: control - go to 7.
- review - go to 12.

12   **Review**

Consider the arrangements for following up actions to remedy health and safety problems.

- If work is outstanding beyond the deadline, consider:
- organisation: control - go to 7;
- adequacy of resources and commitment to health and safety.

- If a second incident occurs before corrections were made, consider:
- mechanisms for prioritising remedial actions in investigation process;
- competence of those prioritising remedial actions - go to 10.

Appendix 6   *Accident incidence and frequency rates*

Accident incidence and frequency rates provide a means of measuring safety performance over time and comparing it with accident statistics published by external sources, such as HSE.

Employers have to keep records of injuries at work and report certain types to the appropriate enforcing authority, usually HSE or a local authority.[23] Reportable injuries include fatal and major injuries to employees, self-employed people and members of the public, and injuries that cause incapacity for work for more than three days to employees and self-employed people ('over-3-day injuries'). Statistical information from these injury reports is collated by HSE and published in the Health and Safety Commission's Annual Report and Health and Safety Statistics Report. The published information gives details of injuries reported from each major sector of industry as classified by the 1992 Standard Industrial Classification.

The accuracy of the nationally collated injury statistics depends on employers complying with the legal reporting requirements. In some industries, under-reporting of injuries by employers is a serious problem. Firms with good record-keeping arrangements in an industry with a high level of under-reporting may therefore find that their injury rates compare unfavourably with the published rates for their industry. The figures in such cases obviously must be interpreted accordingly. Even so, incidence rates can still be used to monitor performance over time and between different departments.

Comparing reportable injury information is just one way of assessing a firm's safety performance. In many firms, particularly those with fewer than 100 employees, reportable injuries represent only a small proportion of the total number of injuries to employees. Records of more minor, non-reportable injuries, and of 'near misses', may also be converted into incidence rates and used to monitor trends over time or between different parts of the operation. Analysis of the data to identify the main causes of injury, for example, can help to identify risks that need to be controlled and prevent further accidents.

Calculation of injury incidence rates

HSE's formula for calculating an annual injury incidence rate is:

$$\frac{\text{Number of reportable injuries in financial year}}{\text{Average number employed during year}} \times 100\,000$$

This gives the rate per 100 000 employees. The formula makes no allowances for variations in part-time employment or overtime. It is an annual calculation and the figures need to be adjusted pro-rata if they cover a shorter period. Such shorter-term rates should be compared only with rates for exactly similar periods - not the national annual rates.

Calculation of injury frequency rates

While HSE calculates injury **incidence rates** per 100 000 employees, some parts of industry prefer to calculate injury **frequency rates**, usually per million hours worked. This method, by counting hours worked rather than the number of employees, avoids distortions which may be caused in the incidence rate calculations by part- and full-time employees and by overtime working. Frequency rates can be calculated for any time period.

The calculation is:

$$\frac{\text{Number of injuries in the period}}{\text{Total hours worked during the period}} \times 1\ 000\ 000$$

References

1   *The costs of accidents at work* (2nd edition) HSG96 HSE Books 1997 ISBN 0 7176 1343 7
    (Out of print)

2   Bird F E and Germain G L *Practical loss control leadership* Institute Publishing (Division of
    International Loss Control Institute), Loganville, Georgia 1985 ISBN 0 88061 054 9

3   *Reducing error and influencing behaviour* HSG48 HSE Books 1999 ISBN 0 7176 2452 8

4   BS EN ISO 14001: 2004 *Environmental management systems - Requirements with guidance for use*

5   BS 8800: 2004 *Occupational health and safety management systems. Guide*

6   Council Regulation (EEC) No 1836/93 of 29 June 1993 allowing voluntary participation by
    companies in the industrial sector in a Community eco-management and audit scheme

7   BS EN ISO 9000-1: 1994 *Quality management and quality assurance standards: Guidelines for selection
    and use*

8   *How to use the model* British Quality Foundation ISBN 1 899358 50 1 (British Quality Foundation,
    32-34 Great Peter Street, London SW1P 2QX Tel: 020 7654 5000)

9   *Total quality management and the management of health and safety* CRR153 HSE Books 1997
    ISBN 0 7176 1455 7 (View online at www.hse.gov.uk)

10 *Developing a safety culture* Confederation of British Industry 1990 ISBN 0852013612

11 ACSNI *Study Group on Human Factors 3rd report: Organising for safety* HSE Books 1993
    ISBN 0 7176 0865 4 (View online at www.hse.gov.uk)

12 *Business re-engineering and health and safety management: Best practice model* CRR 123 HSE Books 1996
    ISBN 0 7176 1302 X

13 *Safety representatives and safety committees* L87 HSE Books 1996 ISBN 0 7176 1220 1

14 *A guide to the Offshore Installations (Safety Representatives and Safety Committees) Regulations 1989*
    L110 HSE Books 1998 ISBN 0 7176 1549 9

15 *A Guide to the Health and Safety (Consultation with Employees) Regulations 1996. Guidance on
    Regulations* L95 HSE Books 1996 ISBN 0 7176 1234 1

16   Health and safety training: What you need to know INDG345 HSE Books 2001

17   Health and safety standards on CD-ROM is available from ENTO Tel: 0116 251 7979, website: www.ento.co.uk

18   Management of health and safety at work. Management of Health and Safety at Work Regulations 1999. Approved Code of Practice and guidance L21 HSE Books 2000 ISBN 0 7176 2488 9

19   Control of substances hazardous to health. The Control of Substances Hazardous to Health Regulations 2002 (as amended). Approved Code of Practice and guidance L5 (Fifth edition) HSE Books 2005 ISBN 0 7176 2981 3

20   Health risk management: A practical guide for managers in small and medium-sized enterprises HSG137 HSE Books 1995 ISBN 0 7176 0905 7

21   5 steps to risk assessment INDG163(rev1) HSE Books 1998

22   A guide to the Offshore Installations (Safety Case) Regulations 1992. Guidance on Regulations L30 HSE Books 1998 ISBN 0 7176 1165 5

23   A guide to the Reporting of Injuries, Diseases and Dangerous Occurrences Regulations 1995 (RIDDOR) L73 HSE Books 1999 ISBN 0 7176 2431 5

24   Dow's fire and explosion index: Hazard classification guide (7th edition) American Institute of Chemical Engineers 1994 ISBN 0816906238

25   Railway safety cases. Railways (Safety Case) Regulations 2000 including 2001 and 2003 amendments. Guidance on Regulations L52 HSE Books 2003 ISBN 0 7176 2186 3

26   Improving compliance with safety procedures: Reducing industrial violations Report from the Human Factors in Reliability Group (HFRG) Violations Sub-Group HSE Books 1995 ISBN 0 7176 0970 7

27   Sulzer-Azaroff B 'The modification of occupational safety behaviour' Journal of Occupational Accidents Nov 1987 Vol 9 No 3 177-197

28   Krause T R The behaviour-based safety process: Managing involvement for an injury-free culture (2nd edition) Van Nostrand Reinhold 1997 ISBN 047128758X

29   *Health and safety climate survey tool* (Electronic publication) HSE Books 1997 ISBN 0 7176 1462 X

30   A *guide to the Gas Safety* (*Management*) *Regulations* 1996 L80 HSE Books 1996 ISBN 0 7176 1159 0 (Out of print)

The future availability and accuracy of the references listed in this publication cannot be guaranteed.

For details of how to obtain HSE priced and free publications, see inside back cover.

British Standards are available from BSI Customer Services, 389 Chiswick High Road, London W4 4AL Tel: 0208 996 9001 Fax: 0208 996 7001.

Printed and published by the Health and Safety Executive   03/06   C150